Lonsdale SCIENCE REVISION GUIDES

INTRODUCTION ...

This guide is matched perfectly to the Modular Double and Single Award Specification B (1536, 1535) from Edexcel and also closely reflects their excellent scheme of work.

The reduction in HIGHER material means that we can combine both tiers in the same volume for greater flexibility. This HIGHER material is clearly indicated by red boxes.

All the material within a module is condensed into a KEY POINTS page both for a last minute recap and to Instlll confidence by demonstrating the size of the task.

Our excellent value workbook matches the guide page for page and is available from the address opposite.

HOW TO USE THIS REVISION GUIDE

- This guide contains everything you need to know and nothing more.
- Don't just read it! Revise actively! Test yourself without looking at the text.
- Tick each section and diagram as you revise it, and the appropriate tick box on the contents page. Use the Key Points pages only for your final run through.

  HIGHER TIER
  > Only revise the 'red boxes' if you are doing Higher Tier. (Ask your teacher about this.)

- And don't forget! You'll need this guide toward the end of year II for your terminal exams.

SOME IMPORTANT FACTS ABOUT YOUR EXAMINATION ...

Your course lasts two years. If you are doing Single Award, you will study only the 6 modules in this guide, whereas Double Award students will also take the 6 modules in VOLUME 2 (7-12).

Each module test covers both Higher and Foundation Tiers and you are expected to answer 24 multiple choice questions in 20 minutes (less difficult than it sounds!)

All your modular tests together contribute a maximum of 30% towards your final exam mark, so it's well worth taking them seriously.

The first Terminal Exam will cover modules 1-6 and will last 90 minutes. If you are doing Single Award this is all you have to face. Double Award students however, have another exam covering modules 7-12 which also lasts 90 minutes. Your Terminal Exam contributes a maximum of 50% of your total marks.

The remaining 20% of available marks is for your coursework.

• CONTENTS

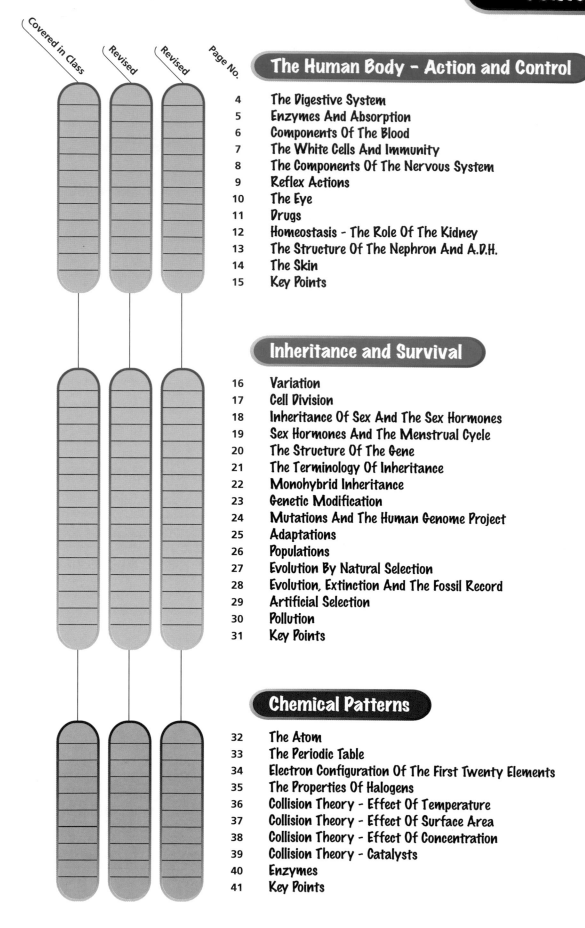

• CONTENTS

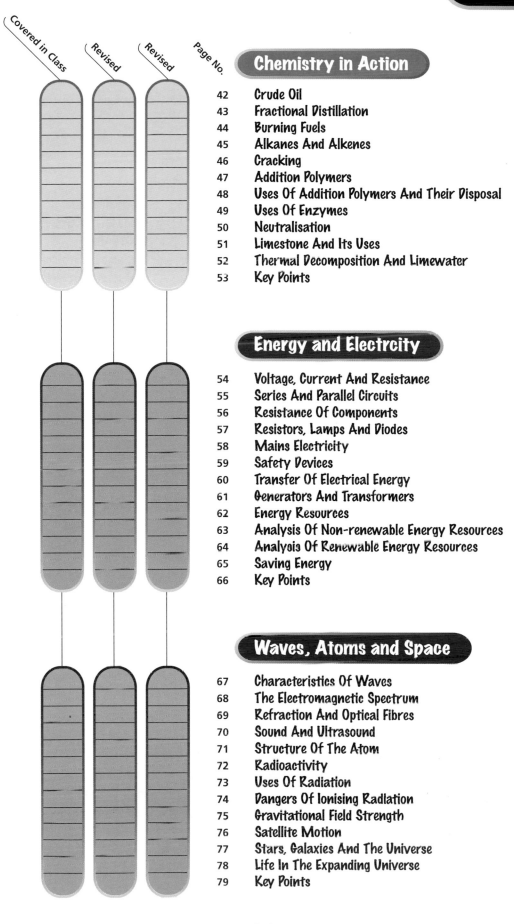

The **DIGESTIVE SYSTEM** is really made up of a long **MUSCULAR TUBE** in which **ENZYMES** speed up (catalyse) the breakdown of **LARGE INSOLUBLE MOLECULES** eg. starch, proteins and fats into **SMALLER SOLUBLE MOLECULES** so that they can pass through the walls of the small intestine and into the bloodstream. Reabsorption of water takes place in the large intestine leaving indigestible food which leaves the body as faeces via the anus.

The Human Digestive System

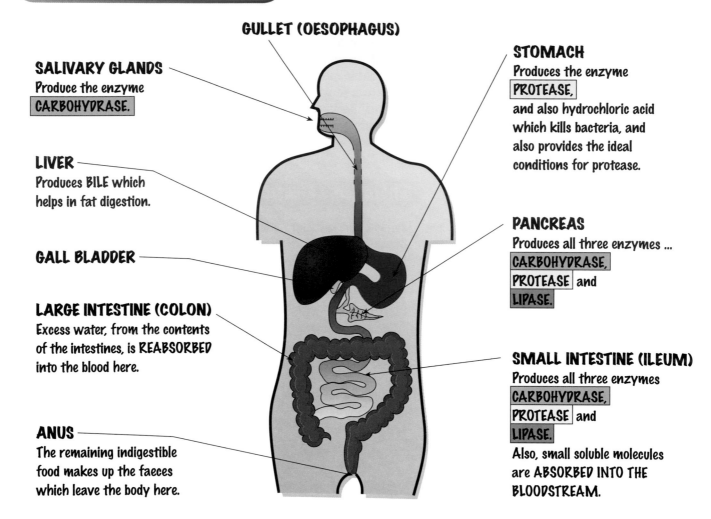

GULLET (OESOPHAGUS)

SALIVARY GLANDS
Produce the enzyme
CARBOHYDRASE.

LIVER
Produces BILE which
helps in fat digestion.

GALL BLADDER

LARGE INTESTINE (COLON)
Excess water, from the contents
of the intestines, is REABSORBED
into the blood here.

ANUS
The remaining indigestible
food makes up the faeces
which leave the body here.

STOMACH
Produces the enzyme
PROTEASE,
and also hydrochloric acid
which kills bacteria, and
also provides the ideal
conditions for protease.

PANCREAS
Produces all three enzymes ...
CARBOHYDRASE,
PROTEASE and
LIPASE.

SMALL INTESTINE (ILEUM)
Produces all three enzymes
CARBOHYDRASE,
PROTEASE and
LIPASE.
Also, small soluble molecules
are ABSORBED INTO THE
BLOODSTREAM.

The Function Of Bile

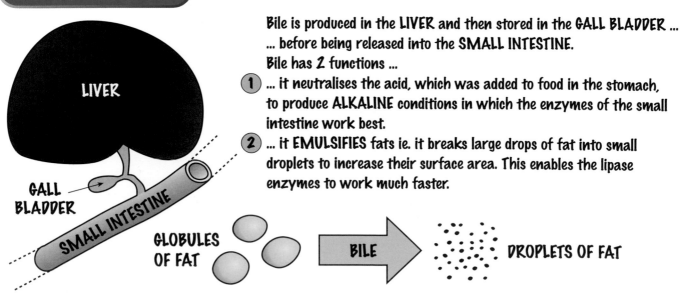

Bile is produced in the **LIVER** and then stored in the **GALL BLADDER** ...
... before being released into the **SMALL INTESTINE**.
Bile has 2 functions ...

(1) ... it neutralises the acid, which was added to food in the stomach, to produce **ALKALINE** conditions in which the enzymes of the small intestine work best.

(2) ... it **EMULSIFIES** fats ie. it breaks large drops of fat into small droplets to increase their surface area. This enables the lipase enzymes to work much faster.

LIVER

GALL BLADDER

SMALL INTESTINE

GLOBULES OF FAT   BILE   DROPLETS OF FAT

Enzyme Summary

Three enzymes PROTEASE, LIPASE and CARBOHYDRASE are produced in four separate regions of the digestive system. They digest proteins, fats and carbohydrates to produce molecules which can be absorbed.

SALIVARY GLANDS

| CARBOHYDRASE | CARBOHYDRATES | ⟶ | SUGARS (e.g. glucose) |

STOMACH

| PROTEASE | PROTEINS | ⟶ | AMINO ACIDS |

PANCREAS
(These enzymes are released into the small intestine).

CARBOHYDRASE	CARBOHYDRATES	⟶	SUGARS (e.g. glucose)
PROTEASE	PROTEINS	⟶	AMINO ACIDS
LIPASE	FATS	⟶	FATTY ACIDS + GLYCEROL

SMALL INTESTINE

CARBOHYDRASE	CARBOHYDRATES	⟶	SUGARS (e.g. glucose)
PROTEASE	PROTEINS	⟶	AMINO ACIDS
LIPASE	FATS	⟶	FATTY ACIDS + GLYCEROL

Absorption In The Small Intestine

The three enzymes catalyse the breakdown of LARGE INSOLUBLE MOLECULES into SMALL SOLUBLE MOLECULES which then diffuse through the walls of the small intestine into the bloodstream.

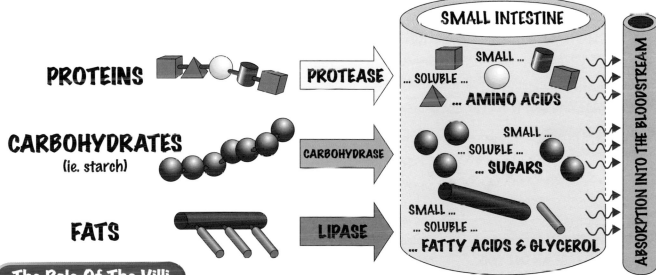

PROTEINS → PROTEASE → SMALL ... ... SOLUBLE ... ... AMINO ACIDS

CARBOHYDRATES (ie. starch) → CARBOHYDRASE → SMALL ... ... SOLUBLE ... ... SUGARS

FATS → LIPASE → SMALL ... ... SOLUBLE ... ... FATTY ACIDS & GLYCEROL

SMALL INTESTINE

ABSORPTION INTO THE BLOODSTREAM

The Role Of The Villi

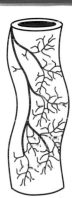

The surface of the small intestine is covered by thousands of finger-like projections called VILLI, each of which contain fairly extensive capillary networks. These help to make the process of absorption more efficient by ...

- ... MASSIVELY INCREASING THE SURFACE AREA ...
- ... PROVIDING A HUGE BLOOD SUPPLY TO TRANSPORT AWAY THE SOLUBLE PRODUCTS OF DIGESTION, and ...
- ... PROVIDING A VERY THIN WALL TO ALLOW EASY DIFFUSION OF AMINO ACIDS, SUGARS, FATTY ACIDS AND GLYCEROL INTO THE BLOODSTREAM.

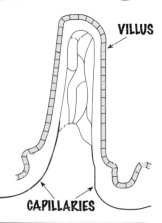

VILLUS

CAPILLARIES

The Blood

If blood is allowed to stand without clotting, it separates out into its 4 components ...

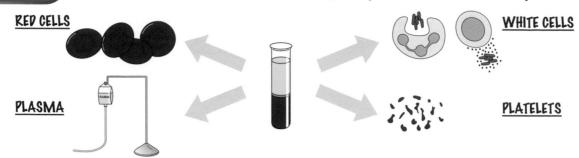

RED CELLS

WHITE CELLS

PLASMA

PLATELETS

The Red Blood Cells

The bi-concave shape of the cells gives them a bigger surface area through which to absorb oxygen.

- They have no nucleus so that they can be packed with HAEMOGLOBIN.
- HAEMOGLOBIN is a substance which combines easily with oxygen when there's plenty of oxygen about.
- In the lungs, where there's lots of oxygen ...
  ... HAEMOGLOBIN + OXYGEN ⟶ OXYHAEMOGLOBIN.
- In the tissues where oxygen is being used up ...
  ... OXYHAEMOGLOBIN ⟶ HAEMOGLOBIN + OXYGEN.
- Haemoglobin's reversible reaction with oxygen ensures that oxygen is transported to where it's needed.

The Plasma

... is a straw-coloured liquid consisting mainly of water, containing a suspension of blood cells.

Plasma transports ...

❶ CARBON DIOXIDE from the organs to the lungs.
❷ SOLUBLE PRODUCTS OF DIGESTION (eg. glucose and amino acids) from the small intestine.
❸ UREA from the liver to the kidneys.
❹ Chemical messengers called HORMONES.
❺ WATER to and from various parts of the body.

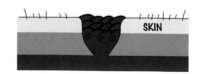

The Platelets

... are tiny pieces of cells which have no nucleus.
They are an important factor in HELPING THE BLOOD TO CLOT when a blood vessel has been damaged.

❶ When the skin is cut the PLATELETS in the blood are exposed to air and RELEASE AN ENZYME.

❷ The enzyme converts a SOLUBLE protein into INSOLUBLE FIBRES of protein called FIBRIN.

❸ The FIBRIN forms a MESH that traps red blood cells and a CLOT forms. This hardens to form a SCAB.

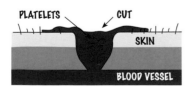
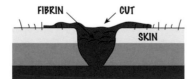

The White Cells

- These cells have a nucleus which may be quite variable in shape.
- Their function is to help to defend the body against invading microbes.
  (Please turn over for more information)

The WHITE BLOOD CELLS form part of the body's IMMUNE SYSTEM.
White blood cells work by ...
1. INGESTING MICROBES.
2. PRODUCING ANTITOXINS to NEUTRALISE TOXINS produced by the microbes.
3. PRODUCING ANTIBODIES to DESTROY PARTICULAR MICROBES.

Ingesting Microbes

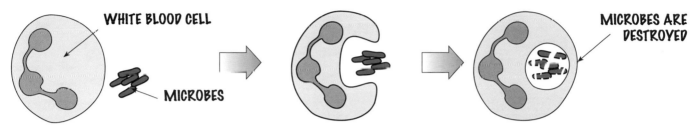

WHITE BLOOD CELL

MICROBES

MICROBES ARE
DESTROYED

Microbes invade the body ...

... the white blood cell starts
to surround the microbes.

The microbes are INGESTED
by the white blood cell.

White cells can actually move out of the capillaries and into the surrounding tissues so that they can reach the site of infections. Here they ingest microbes and eventually die, forming pus. This type of white cell is called a PHAGOCYTE.

Producing Antitoxins

White blood cells produce ANTITOXINS which NEUTRALISE HARMFUL TOXINS (poisons) produced by microbes.

Producing Antibodies

- WHITE BLOOD CELLS recognise the microbes as ANTIGENS (foreign bodies) ...
  ... and produce ANTIBODIES to destroy the ANTIGENS. (Often by making them clump together!).
- The reason we feel ILL is because it takes TIME for the WHITE BLOOD CELLS to produce ANTIBODIES to the microbes.
- The PRODUCTION OF ANTIBODIES is much faster if a person has already had the infectious disease.
  The WHITE BLOOD CELLS seem to 'remember' the antigen and in the future can produce ANTIBODIES more rapidly providing the person with a NATURAL IMMUNITY. This type of white cell is called a LYMPHOCYTE.

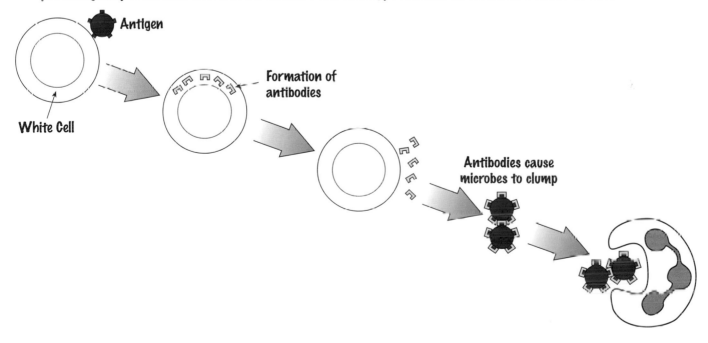

Antigen

Formation of
antibodies

White Cell

Antibodies cause
microbes to clump

Reaction And Coordination

- The nervous system consists of the BRAIN, the SPINAL CORD, the PAIRED PERIPHERAL NERVES and RECEPTORS.
- It allows organisms to REACT TO THEIR SURROUNDINGS and ...
    ... to COORDINATE THEIR BEHAVIOUR.
- The FIVE SENSES, namely SEEING, HEARING, TASTING, SMELLING and TOUCHING
    play a very important part in these processes.

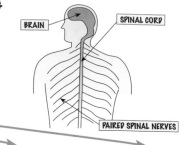

Components Of The Nervous System

NERVOUS SYSTEM

BRAIN   SPINAL CORD   RELAY NEURONES   SENSORY NEURONES   MOTOR NEURONES   RECEPTORS

The Central Nervous System (C.N.S)

These make up the paired spinal nerves of the Peripheral Nervous System.

The Three Types Of Nerve Cell (Neurone)

1. MOTOR NEURONE

DIRECTION OF IMPULSE ⟶
(away from cell body)

2. SENSORY NEURONE

DIRECTION OF IMPULSE ⟶
(towards cell body)

3. RELAY NEURONE

NEURONES are SPECIALLY ADAPTED CELLS that can carry an ELECTRICAL SIGNAL.
eg. a NERVE IMPULSE.

Nucleus

Nerve Fibre

Muscle Fibre
(the effector)

Cell Body

A MOTOR NEURONE

- MOTOR NEURONES are specially adapted to carry out their function in the following ways:
  They are ELONGATED (long) to MAKE CONNECTIONS from one part of the body to another.
  They have an INSULATING SHEATH which SPEEDS UP THE NERVE IMPULSE.
  They have BRANCHED ENDINGS which allow a SINGLE NEURONE to act on MANY MUSCLE FIBRES.
  The cell body has many connections to allow communication with other neurones.

Nerve Pathways

Neurones pass information into and out of the Central Nervous System.

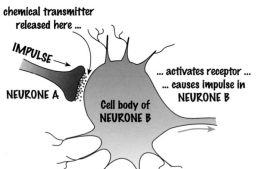

chemical transmitter
released here ...

IMPULSE ⟶

NEURONE A

Cell body of
NEURONE B

... activates receptor ...
... causes impulse in
NEURONE B

- Neurones do NOT TOUCH EACH OTHER ...
- ... there is a very small gap between them ...
- ... called a SYNAPSE.
- When an electrical impulse reaches this gap via neurone A
  a CHEMICAL TRANSMITTER ...
- ... is released and activates receptors on NEURONE B ...
- ... which causes an electrical IMPULSE to be generated
  in NEURONE B.
- The CHEMICAL TRANSMITTER is then IMMEDIATELY DESTROYED.

As a result of the connections between neurones, pathways exist which control certain reflexes in our bodies.

The Iris Reflex

The pupil of the human eye can open and close in order to regulate the amount of light entering the eye.

RESPONSE TO DIM LIGHT   **RESPONSE TO MODERATE LIGHT**   **RESPONSE TO BRIGHT LIGHT**

In **DIM LIGHT** ...

... **RADIAL MUSCLES IN THE IRIS CONTRACT** ...

... and **CIRCULAR MUSCLES RELAX** ...

... **INCREASING THE SIZE OF THE PUPIL.**

In **BRIGHT LIGHT** ...

... **CIRCULAR MUSCLES IN THE IRIS CONTRACT** ...

... and **RADIAL MUSCLES RELAX** ...

... **DECREASING THE SIZE OF THE PUPIL.**

This is a **REFLEX** and occurs automatically, without having to think about it.

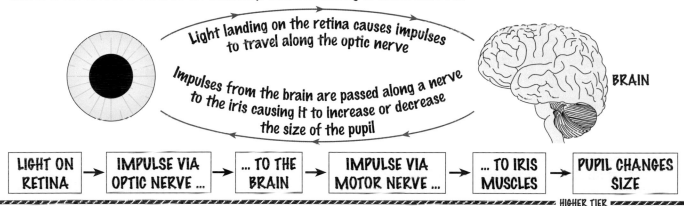

Light landing on the retina causes impulses to travel along the optic nerve

Impulses from the brain are passed along a nerve to the iris causing it to increase or decrease the size of the pupil

BRAIN

| LIGHT ON RETINA | → | IMPULSE VIA OPTIC NERVE ... | → | ... TO THE BRAIN | → | IMPULSE VIA MOTOR NERVE ... | → | ... TO IRIS MUSCLES | → | PUPIL CHANGES SIZE |

— HIGHER TIER —

The Reflex Arc

Besides the iris reflex, there are many other reflexes in the human body. Sometimes 'Conscious Action' would be too slow to prevent harm to the body eg. putting your hand on a hot plate! 'Reflex Action' speeds up the response time by missing out the brain. The spinal cord acts as the coordinator and passes impulses directly from a sensory neurone to a motor neurone via a **RELAY NEURONE** which 'short-circuits' the brain. This is called a **REFLEX ARC**.

STAGES OF REFLEX ACTION

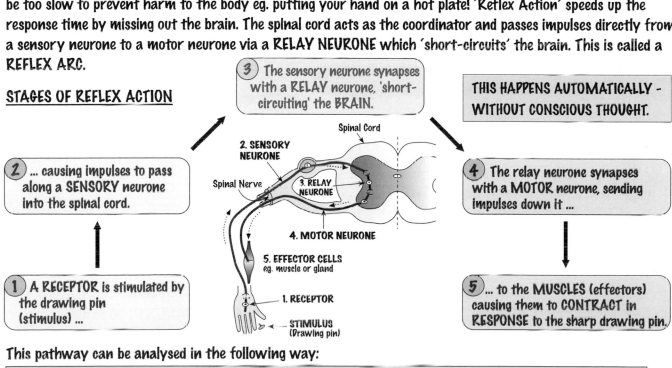

③ The sensory neurone synapses with a RELAY neurone, 'short-circuiting' the BRAIN.

THIS HAPPENS AUTOMATICALLY - WITHOUT CONSCIOUS THOUGHT.

② ... causing impulses to pass along a SENSORY neurone into the spinal cord.

④ The relay neurone synapses with a MOTOR neurone, sending impulses down it ...

① A RECEPTOR is stimulated by the drawing pin (stimulus) ...

⑤ ... to the MUSCLES (effectors) causing them to CONTRACT in RESPONSE to the sharp drawing pin.

This pathway can be analysed in the following way:

STIMULUS ⇨	RECEPTOR ⇨	SENSORY NEURONE ⇨	CENTRAL NERVOUS SYSTEM ⇨	MOTOR NEURONE ⇨	EFFECTOR ⇨	RESPONSE
Drawing pin	Pain receptor	Nerve from receptor	Relay neurone in spinal cord	Nerve to muscle	Muscle in hand	Withdraw hand

The Structure Of The Eye

The Eye is quite a complicated sense organ which focuses light onto light-sensitive receptor cells in the retina. These are then stimulated and cause nerve impulses to pass along sensory neurones to the brain.

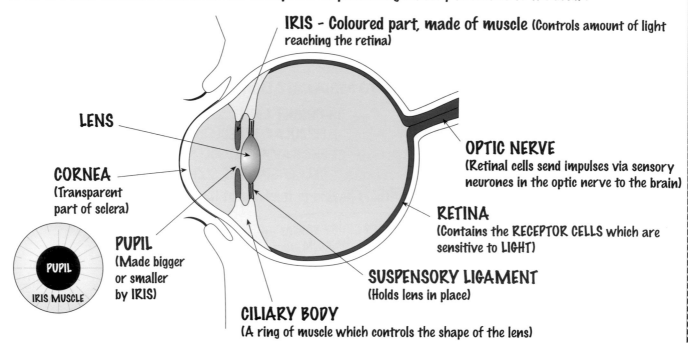

IRIS - Coloured part, made of muscle (Controls amount of light reaching the retina)

LENS

CORNEA
(Transparent part of sclera)

OPTIC NERVE
(Retinal cells send impulses via sensory neurones in the optic nerve to the brain)

RETINA
(Contains the RECEPTOR CELLS which are sensitive to LIGHT)

PUPIL
(Made bigger or smaller by IRIS)

PUPIL

IRIS MUSCLE

SUSPENSORY LIGAMENT
(Holds lens in place)

CILIARY BODY
(A ring of muscle which controls the shape of the lens)

The CORNEA and the LENS focus rays of light ...
... so that an IMAGE is formed on the RETINA.

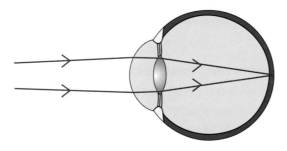

Rays of light are BENT (REFRACTED) BY THE CORNEA.
The rays of light are then ...
... further BENT (REFRACTED) BY THE LENS ...
... to produce a CLEAR IMAGE ...
... on the RETINA.

Focusing On Objects At Different Distances

DISTANT OBJECT

- CILIARY BODY RELAXES.
- SUSPENSORY LIGAMENTS PULL TIGHT.
- LENS IS PULLED 'THINNER', and ...
- ... LIGHT ISN'T BENT AS MUCH.

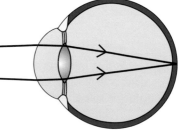

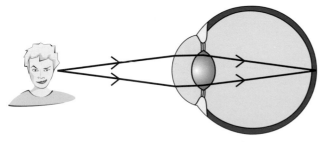

NEAR OBJECT

- CILIARY BODY CONTRACTS.
- SUSPENSORY LIGAMENTS GO SLACK ...
- ... ALLOWING LENS TO BECOME 'FATTER', ...
- ... BENDING LIGHT MUCH MORE.

It's important to understand that the FLUID in the eye retains the shape of the eye and keeps the SUSPENSORY LIGAMENTS TIGHT. The CILIARY BODY has to work to overcome this tension which is why eyes get tired after lots of focusing on near objects, eg. reading.

DRUGS are chemical substances which ALTER THE WAY THE BODY WORKS.
Some drugs can be obtained from LIVING THINGS, others are SYNTHETIC (MAN-MADE).
Some drugs are called MEDICINES and these are taken to CURE ILLNESSES or EASE THE SYMPTOMS
produced during an illness. Examples include PAINKILLERS and ANTIBIOTICS (which destroy bacteria and some
other microbes).

Alcohol, Tobacco And Solvents

NAME OF DRUG	EFFECTS
ALCOHOL Contains the chemical ethanol.	• ALCOHOL is a DEPRESSANT and causes SLOW REACTIONS. • ALCOHOL can lead to a LACK OF SELF CONTROL. • EXCESS can lead to UNCONSCIOUSNESS and even COMA or DEATH. • The LONG TERM effects of ALCOHOL can be LIVER DAMAGE (due to the liver removing the toxic alcohol from the body) or BRAIN DAMAGE.
TOBACCO Contains the chemicals Tar Carbon Monoxide Nicotine (which is addictive) 	TOBACCO is a MAJOR CAUSE of HEALTH PROBLEMS: • EMPHYSEMA - alveoli damage due to excessive coughing. • BRONCHITIS - increased infection due to INCREASED mucus production. • PROBLEMS IN PREGNANCY - Tobacco smoke contains carbon monoxide which combines irreversibly with the haemoglobin in red blood cells, reducing the oxygen-carrying capacity of the blood. In pregnant women this can deprive a foetus of oxygen and lead to a low birth mass. • ARTERIAL and HEART DISEASE - damage to blood vessels which can lead to HEART ATTACKS, STROKES and even AMPUTATIONS.
SOLVENTS Different kinds of vapours are given off by solvents.	• SOLVENTS lead to SLOWED REACTIONS and HALLUCINATIONS. • SOLVENTS can affect a person's BEHAVIOUR and cause CHARACTER CHANGES. • SOLVENTS may cause PERMANENT DAMAGE to the LUNGS, LIVER, BRAIN or KIDNEYS.

Effects Of Other Drugs

Caffeine   This is a mild stimulant found in tea, coffee and cocoa. Too much can keep you awake and make you a little highly strung but you're unlikely to come to too much harm.

Paracetamol   This is a mild analgesic (painkiller) and anti inflammatory. It also helps to lower body temperature. However, great care must be taken not to exceed the recommended dosages since this can lead to liver failure. In addition, it doesn't mix well with alcohol; the two tending to form a toxic compound.

Barbiturates   These were used as sedatives because they have a depressant effect on the Central Nervous System. Their clinical use is now reduced due to the toxic side effects. They can also be highly addictive.

Heroin is a derivative of morphine and as such is a powerful analgesic (painkiller). Consequently it is much used by medical personnel to control pain especially in the case of terminally ill patients. The downside is that it is highly addictive and its mis-use is one of the great sadnesses of modern life.
In addition to making its users hopelessly dependent it carries the risk of spreading viruses such as HIV due to the sharing of hypodermic syringes. WHATEVER ELSE YOU MAY LEARN FROM THIS GUIDE PLEASE ENSURE THAT YOU ALWAYS SAY NO TO DRUGS, AND THAT YOU ARE SENSIBLE ABOUT ALCOHOL USE.

Homeostasis

Homeostasis is the maintenance of a CONSTANT INTERNAL ENVIRONMENT, by balancing bodily INPUTS and OUTPUTS and removing waste products. Humans need to be at the CORRECT TEMPERATURE, and also need to maintain the correct WATER CONTENT. In addition, they must remove UREA, which is formed in the liver as a result of the breakdown of excess amino acids. (Excess amino acids can't be stored.)

The kidney is an important homeostatic organ and controls the water content of the body and removes urea. The skin also has a homeostatic role in that it helps to maintain body temperature within narrow limits.

The Urinary System

The MAJOR ORGAN in the URINARY SYSTEM is the KIDNEY.

The job of the KIDNEY is to remove EXCESS WATER and the waste substance UREA from the body.

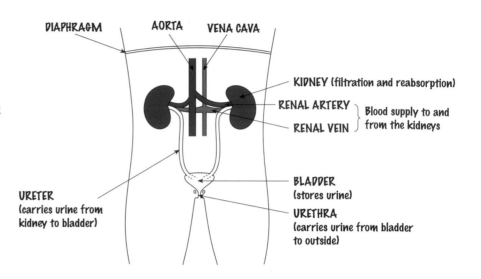

DIAPHRAGM   AORTA   VENA CAVA

KIDNEY (filtration and reabsorption)

RENAL ARTERY
RENAL VEIN } Blood supply to and from the kidneys

URETER (carries urine from kidney to bladder)

BLADDER (stores urine)

URETHRA (carries urine from bladder to outside)

The Kidney

- The kidney is made up of two important tissues, BLOOD VESSELS and TUBULES.
- BLOOD VESSELS take the blood through the kidney where unwanted substances ...
- ... end up in millions of tiny TUBULES which eventually join together to form one tube ...
- ... the URETER which leaves the kidney and ends up at the BLADDER.

THE KIDNEY REGULATES THE AMOUNT OF WATER AND IONS IN THE BLOOD AND REMOVES <u>ALL</u> UREA.

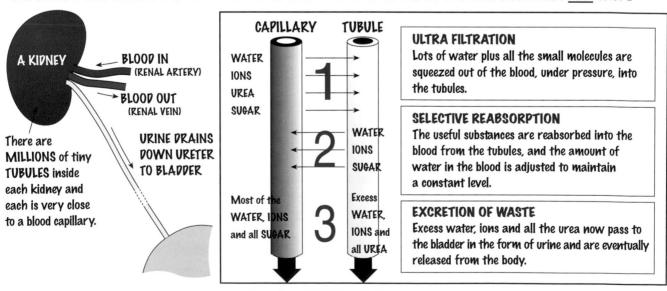

A KIDNEY

BLOOD IN (RENAL ARTERY)

BLOOD OUT (RENAL VEIN)

There are MILLIONS of tiny TUBULES inside each kidney and each is very close to a blood capillary.

URINE DRAINS DOWN URETER TO BLADDER

CAPILLARY   TUBULE

WATER
IONS
UREA
SUGAR

1

2

WATER
IONS
SUGAR

Most of the WATER, IONS and all SUGAR

3

Excess WATER, IONS and all UREA

ULTRA FILTRATION
Lots of water plus all the small molecules are squeezed out of the blood, under pressure, into the tubules.

SELECTIVE REABSORPTION
The useful substances are reabsorbed into the blood from the tubules, and the amount of water in the blood is adjusted to maintain a constant level.

EXCRETION OF WASTE
Excess water, ions and all the urea now pass to the bladder in the form of urine and are eventually released from the body.

So, ... in principle there are THREE STAGES to learn ...

❶ ... nearly everything is SQUEEZED OUT of the blood into the TUBULES ...
❷ ... the substances we want to keep are REABSORBED back into the blood ...
❸ ... unwanted substances are RELEASED as URINE.

HIGHER TIER

Structure Of The Nephron

The nephron is the functional unit of the kidney and each kidney contains around a million nephrons. Each nephron drains into a collecting tubule and all the collecting tubules release urine into one common tube, the ureter, which drains urine away from the kidney and into the bladder.

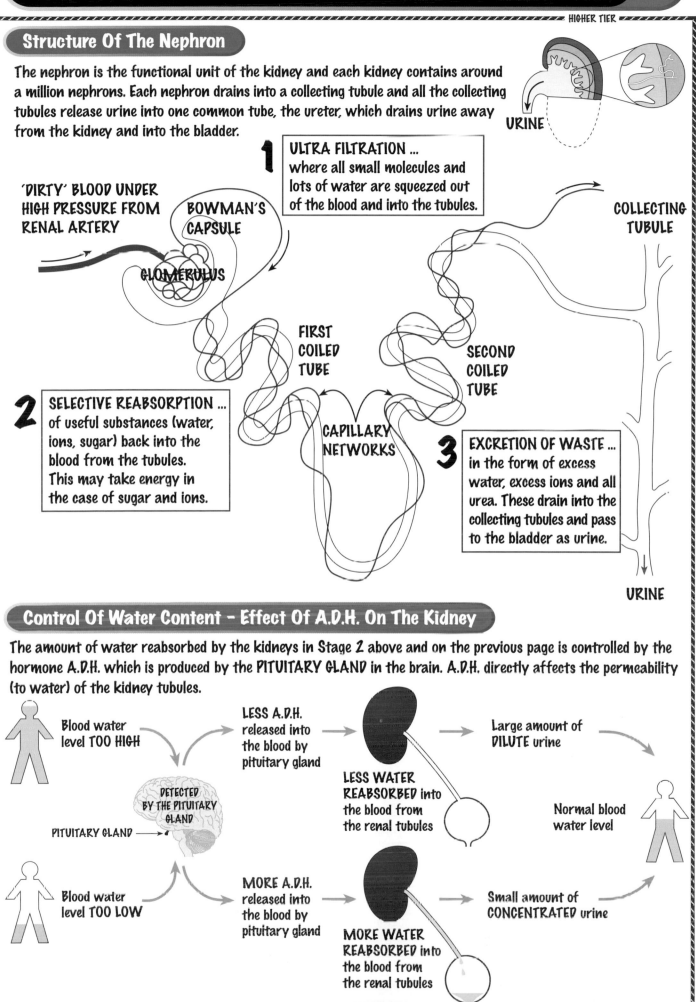

URINE

1 ULTRA FILTRATION ... where all small molecules and lots of water are squeezed out of the blood and into the tubules.

'DIRTY' BLOOD UNDER HIGH PRESSURE FROM RENAL ARTERY

BOWMAN'S CAPSULE

GLOMERULUS

COLLECTING TUBULE

FIRST COILED TUBE

SECOND COILED TUBE

2 SELECTIVE REABSORPTION ... of useful substances (water, ions, sugar) back into the blood from the tubules. This may take energy in the case of sugar and ions.

CAPILLARY NETWORKS

3 EXCRETION OF WASTE ... in the form of excess water, excess ions and all urea. These drain into the collecting tubules and pass to the bladder as urine.

URINE

Control Of Water Content - Effect Of A.D.H. On The Kidney

The amount of water reabsorbed by the kidneys in Stage 2 above and on the previous page is controlled by the hormone A.D.H. which is produced by the PITUITARY GLAND in the brain. A.D.H. directly affects the permeability (to water) of the kidney tubules.

Blood water level TOO HIGH

DETECTED BY THE PITUITARY GLAND

PITUITARY GLAND →

LESS A.D.H. released into the blood by pituitary gland

LESS WATER REABSORBED into the blood from the renal tubules

Large amount of DILUTE urine

Normal blood water level

Blood water level TOO LOW

MORE A.D.H. released into the blood by pituitary gland

MORE WATER REABSORBED into the blood from the renal tubules

Small amount of CONCENTRATED urine

Structure Of The Skin

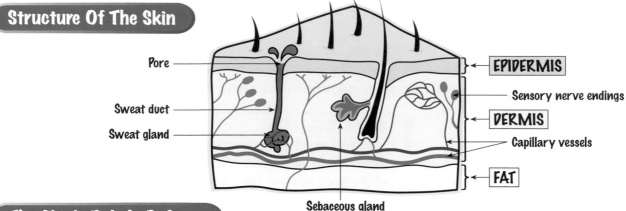

Pore
Sweat duct
Sweat gland

EPIDERMIS
Sensory nerve endings
DERMIS
Capillary vessels
FAT

Sebaceous gland

The Skin's Role In Defence

The skin acts as a physical barrier to the environment and prevents, as far as possible ...

- PUNCTURE due to physical injury, friction or continual flexing.
- DRYING OUT. The epidermis is waterproof and the oil from the sebaceous glands assists this.
- ENTRY OF INFECTION due to bacteria and viruses.
- DAMAGE FROM U-V LIGHT. Pigment in tanned skin blocks out some U-V light.

The outer layer of the epidermis consists mainly of dead cells which are kept supple by regular secretions from the sebaceous glands. This forms the real barrier.

The Skin As Part Of The Nervous System

The skin has sensory nerve endings scattered all over it. These nerve endings are highly specialised to detect PAIN, TOUCH, PRESSURE and TEMPERATURE. These nerve endings are concentrated in areas like the fingertips, lips and the tip of the nose and are less frequent in areas such as the back of the hand and thigh. The presence of these receptors enables us to detect changes in the external environment and relay them to the brain.

The Skin's Role In Temperature Control

Since enzymes work best at 37°C (in humans), it is essential that the body remains very close to this temperature.

- MONITORING AND CONTROL is done by the THERMO-REGULATORY CENTRE in the BRAIN ...
  ... which has receptors which are sensitive to the temperature of the blood flowing through it.
- There are also temperature receptors in the skin which provide information about skin temperature.

CORE TEMP. TOO HIGH   CORE TEMP. TOO LOW

THERMO-REGULATORY
CENTRE

- BLOOD VESSELS IN SKIN DILATE (become wider) CAUSING GREATER HEAT LOSS.
- SWEAT GLANDS RELEASE SWEAT (mainly water and salts) WHICH EVAPORATES, REMOVING HEAT FROM THE SKIN.

- BLOOD VESSELS IN SKIN CONSTRICT (become narrower) REDUCING HEAT LOSS.
- MUSCLES START TO 'SHIVER' CAUSING HEAT ENERGY TO BE RELEASED VIA RESPIRATION IN CELLS.

= HIGHER TIER =

Vasoconstriction And Vasodilation

When surface vessels are dilated, heat is lost through radiation and convection as well as evaporation.

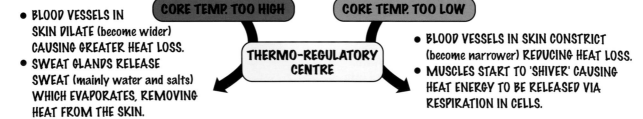

RADIATED HEAT   SWEAT

GREATER BLOOD FLOW THROUGH SUPERFICIAL CAPILLARIES   SWEAT GLAND

SWEATING STOPPED

REDUCED BLOOD FLOW THROUGH SUPERFICIAL CAPILLARIES   SWEAT GLAND

IN HOT CONDITIONS SHUNT VESSEL CLOSED (VASODILATION)   IN COLD CONDITIONS SHUNT VESSEL OPEN (VASOCONSTRICTION)

DIGESTIVE SYSTEM, ENZYMES AND ABSORPTION

Enzymes break down large molecules into smaller soluble molecules.

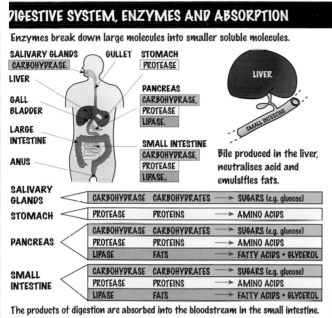

SALIVARY GLANDS — CARBOHYDRASE.
GULLET
STOMACH — PROTEASE
LIVER
PANCREAS — CARBOHYDRASE, PROTEASE, LIPASE.
GALL BLADDER
LARGE INTESTINE
SMALL INTESTINE — CARBOHYDRASE, PROTEASE, LIPASE..
ANUS

LIVER
SMALL INTESTINE

Bile produced in the liver, neutralises acid and emulsifies fats.

SALIVARY GLANDS			
	CARBOHYDRASE	CARBOHYDRATES →	SUGARS (e.g. glucose)

STOMACH			
	PROTEASE	PROTEINS →	AMINO ACIDS

PANCREAS			
	CARBOHYDRASE	CARBOHYDRATES →	SUGARS (e.g. glucose)
	PROTEASE	PROTEINS →	AMINO ACIDS
	LIPASE	FATS →	FATTY ACIDS + GLYCEROL

SMALL INTESTINE			
	CARBOHYDRASE	CARBOHYDRATES →	SUGARS (e.g. glucose)
	PROTEASE	PROTEINS →	AMINO ACIDS
	LIPASE	FATS →	FATTY ACIDS + GLYCEROL

The products of digestion are absorbed into the bloodstream in the small intestine.

THE BLOOD AND IMMUNITY

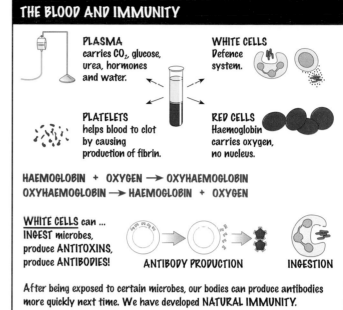

PLASMA carries CO_2, glucose, urea, hormones and water.

WHITE CELLS Defence system.

PLATELETS helps blood to clot by causing production of fibrin.

RED CELLS Haemoglobin carries oxygen, no nucleus.

HAEMOGLOBIN + OXYGEN → OXYHAEMOGLOBIN
OXYHAEMOGLOBIN → HAEMOGLOBIN + OXYGEN

WHITE CELLS can ... INGEST microbes, produce ANTITOXINS, produce ANTIBODIES!

ANTIBODY PRODUCTION   INGESTION

After being exposed to certain microbes, our bodies can produce antibodies more quickly next time. We have developed NATURAL IMMUNITY.

THE NERVOUS SYSTEM

NERVOUS SYSTEM

BRAIN   SPINAL CORD   RELAY NEURONES   SENSORY NEURONES   MOTOR NEURONES   RECEPTORS

- NEURONES are well adapted to their function because they are LONG, BRANCHED and have an INSULATING SHEATH.

Neurones connect with other neurones via synapses.
These are gaps which can be bridged via the production of a chemical transmitter.

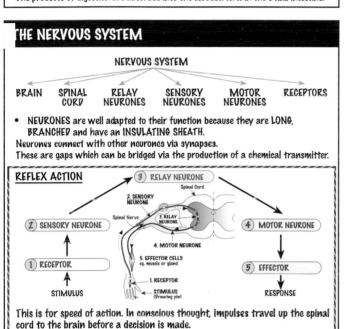

REFLEX ACTION

③ RELAY NEURONE
Spinal Cord
2. SENSORY NEURONE
Spinal Nerve
3. RELAY NEURONE
① RECEPTOR
② SENSORY NEURONE
④ MOTOR NEURONE
4. MOTOR NEURONE
5. EFFECTOR CELLS eg. muscle or gland
⑤ EFFECTOR
1. RECEPTOR
STIMULUS (Drawing pin)
STIMULUS
RESPONSE

This is for speed of action. In conscious thought, impulses travel up the spinal cord to the brain before a decision is made.

THE EYE AND DRUG USE

THE EYE

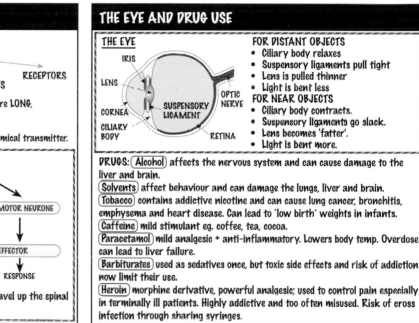

IRIS
LENS
CORNEA
CILIARY BODY
SUSPENSORY LIGAMENT
OPTIC NERVE
RETINA

FOR DISTANT OBJECTS
- Ciliary body relaxes
- Suspensory ligaments pull tight
- Lens is pulled thinner
- Light is bent less

FOR NEAR OBJECTS
- Ciliary body contracts.
- Suspensory ligaments go slack.
- Lens becomes 'fatter'.
- Light is bent more.

DRUGS: (Alcohol) affects the nervous system and can cause damage to the liver and brain.
(Solvents) affect behaviour and can damage the lungs, liver and brain.
(Tobacco) contains addictive nicotine and can cause lung cancer, bronchitis, emphysema and heart disease. Can lead to 'low birth' weights in infants.
(Caffeine) mild stimulant eg. coffee, tea, cocoa.
(Paracetamol) mild analgesic + anti-inflammatory. Lowers body temp. Overdose can lead to liver failure.
(Barbiturates) used as sedatives once, but toxic side effects and risk of addiction now limit their use.
(Heroin) morphine derivative, powerful analgesic; used to control pain especially in terminally ill patients. Highly addictive and too often misused. Risk of cross infection through sharing syringes.

CONTROLLING INTERNAL ENVIRONMENT

ION, UREA + WATER CONTENT

Between the vessels and the tubules, the following three processes occur ...

① ULTRA FILTRATION ② SELECTIVE REABSORPTION ③ EXCRETION OF WASTE

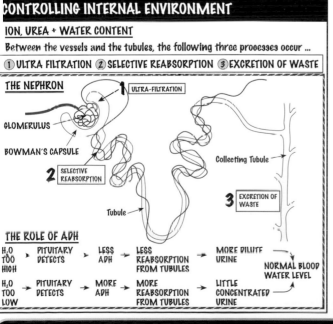

THE NEPHRON

ULTRA-FILTRATION
GLOMERULUS
BOWMAN'S CAPSULE
2 SELECTIVE REABSORPTION
Collecting Tubule
3 EXCRETION OF WASTE
Tubule

THE ROLE OF ADH

H_2O TOO HIGH → PITUITARY DETECTS → LESS ADH → LESS REABSORPTION FROM TUBULES → MORE DILUTE URINE → NORMAL BLOOD WATER LEVEL

H_2O TOO LOW → PITUITARY DETECTS → MORE ADH → MORE REABSORPTION FROM TUBULES → LITTLE CONCENTRATED URINE

THE SKIN

STRUCTURE ...

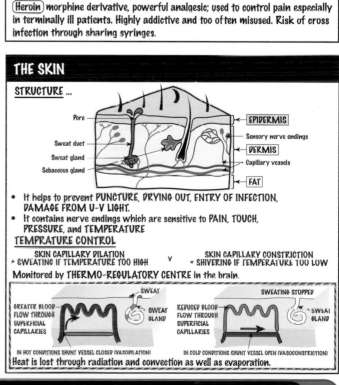

Pore
Sweat duct
Sweat gland
Sebaceous gland
EPIDERMIS
Sensory nerve endings
DERMIS
Capillary vessels
FAT

- It helps to prevent PUNCTURE, DRYING OUT, ENTRY OF INFECTION, DAMAGE FROM U-V LIGHT.
- It contains nerve endings which are sensitive to PAIN, TOUCH, PRESSURE, and TEMPERATURE

TEMPRATURE CONTROL

SKIN CAPILLARY DILATION + SWEATING IF TEMPERATURE TOO HIGH   v   SKIN CAPILLARY CONSTRICTION + SHIVERING IF TEMPERATURE TOO LOW

Monitored by THERMO-REGULATORY CENTRE in the brain.

SWEAT
GREATER BLOOD FLOW THROUGH SUPERFICIAL CAPILLARIES
SWEAT GLAND
IN HOT CONDITIONS SHUNT VESSEL CLOSED (VASODILATION)

SWEATING STOPPED
REDUCED BLOOD FLOW THROUGH SUPERFICIAL CAPILLARIES
SWEAT GLAND
IN COLD CONDITIONS SHUNT VESSEL OPEN (VASOCONSTRICTION)

Heat is lost through radiation and convection as well as evaporation.

Causes Of Variation

Differences between individuals of the same species is described as VARIATION.
Variation may be due to ...

- ... GENETIC CAUSES because of the different genes they have inherited, or ...
- ... ENVIRONMENTAL CAUSES because of the conditions in which they have developed.

Inheritance v Environment

There has been lively debate for many years over the relative importance of genetic and environmental factors in determining human attributes. This is often referred to as the 'Nature verses Nurture' argument.

	GENETIC FACTORS	ENVIRONMENTAL FACTORS
INTELLIGENCE	• The physical structure of the brain and nerve connections. • A person's natural ability in a subject??	• Quality of schooling. • Parental support. • Life experiences.
SPORTING ABILITY	• A person's natural physique/body structure. • A person's natural sporting ability and co-ordination.	• Good coaching and support. • Quality of facilities and the opportunity to practice.

People argue the case for both of these factors, however usually ...

> **VARIATION IS DUE TO A COMBINATION OF GENETIC AND ENVIRONMENTAL CAUSES**

Environmental Effect On Birthweight

The data alongside shows the effect of diet (in terms of energy intake) and smoking on the birthweight and birth length of babies. The figures are adjusted to take into account the different sizes of the mothers.

These figures clearly show that smoking (an environmental factor) reduces the length and weight of newborn babies.

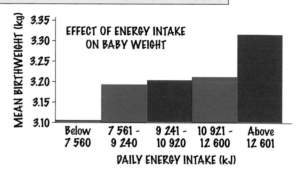

EFFECT OF ENERGY INTAKE ON BABY WEIGHT

MEAN BIRTHWEIGHT (kg)

DAILY ENERGY INTAKE (kJ): Below 7 560 | 7 561 - 9 240 | 9 241 - 10 920 | 10 921 - 12 600 | Above 12 601

	SMOKERS	NON-SMOKERS
AVE. BIRTHWEIGHT (g)	-94	+56
AVE. BIRTH LENGTH (cm)	-0.57	+0.34

Effect Of Reproduction On Variation

SEXUAL REPRODUCTION means LOADS OF VARIATION because ...

... genetic information from two parents is 'mixed together' ...

... when the male (sperm) and female (egg) gametes fuse!!

The sperm contains 23 chromosomes from the father (the HAPLOID number) while the egg contains 23 chromosomes from the mother.

The fusion of these two cells produces a ZYGOTE with 23 <u>pairs</u> of chromosomes (or 46 chromosomes, the DIPLOID number). All the body cells produced from this one cell will also be DIPLOID.

23
HAPLOID

23
HAPLOID

46
DIPLOID

(23 pairs actually!)

ASEXUAL REPRODUCTION means NO VARIATION AT ALL because ...

... only one individual is needed for it to take place, so ...

... genetically identical individuals known as CLONES are produced.

Bacteria reproducing ASEXUALLY

Mitosis

In mitosis a cell divides to produce <u>two</u> cells with identical sets of chromosomes. This happens in order to produce new cells for GROWTH and REPAIR or REPLACEMENT of tissues.

PARENTAL CELL WITH TWO PAIRS OF CHROMOSOMES.

EACH CHROMOSOME <u>REPLICATES</u> ITSELF.

EACH 'DAUGHTER' CELL HAS THE <u>SAME NUMBER OF CHROMOSOMES AS THE PARENTAL CELL</u>, AND CONTAINS THE SAME GENES AS THE PARENTAL CELL.

THE REPLICAS NOW SEPARATE FROM THE ORIGINALS AND THE CELL DIVIDES FOR THE ONLY TIME.

Meiosis

In meiosis a DIPLOID cell divides twice to produce <u>four</u> HAPLOID cells with genetically different sets of chromosomes. This happens in sexually reproducing organisms to produce GAMETES.

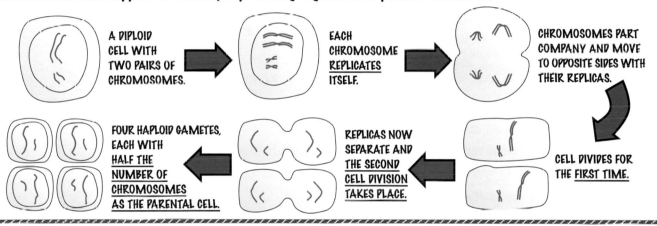

A DIPLOID CELL WITH TWO PAIRS OF CHROMOSOMES.

EACH CHROMOSOME <u>REPLICATES</u> ITSELF.

CHROMOSOMES PART COMPANY AND MOVE TO OPPOSITE SIDES WITH THEIR REPLICAS.

FOUR HAPLOID GAMETES, EACH WITH HALF THE NUMBER OF CHROMOSOMES AS THE PARENTAL CELL.

REPLICAS NOW SEPARATE AND THE SECOND CELL DIVISION TAKES PLACE.

CELL DIVIDES FOR THE <u>FIRST TIME</u>.

Fertilisation

The fusion of haploid male and female gametes is called fertilisation and produces a diploid ZYGOTE.

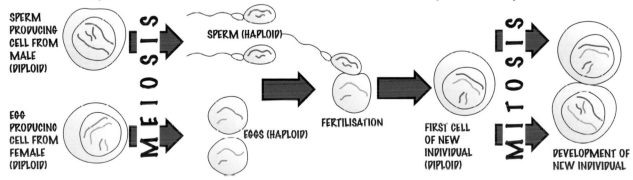

SPERM PRODUCING CELL FROM MALE (DIPLOID)

MEIOSIS

SPERM (HAPLOID)

EGG PRODUCING CELL FROM FEMALE (DIPLOID)

MEIOSIS

EGGS (HAPLOID)

FERTILISATION

FIRST CELL OF NEW INDIVIDUAL (DIPLOID)

MITOSIS

DEVELOPMENT OF NEW INDIVIDUAL

SEXUAL REPRODUCTION PROMOTES VARIATION, because ...

1. The GAMETES (eggs + sperm) are produced by MEIOSIS, WHICH 'SHUFFLES' THE GENES.

2. Gametes FUSE randomly, with ONE OF EACH PAIR OF GENES COMING FROM EACH PARENT.

3. The genes may be DIFFERENT ALLELES (see page P.21) and so produce DIFFERENT CHARACTERISTICS.

Inheritance Of Sex – The Sex Chromosomes

- Humans have **23** pairs of CHROMOSOMES...
- ...of which one pair are the SEX CHROMOSOMES.

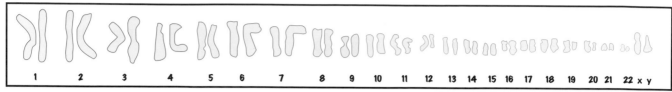

1	2	3	4	5	6	7	8	9	10	11	12	13	14	15	16	17	18	19	20	21	22	x y

- In females these are IDENTICAL and are called the X chromosomes.
- In males ONE IS MUCH SHORTER THAN THE OTHER and they're called the X and Y chromosomes (Y being the shorter).

THE POSSIBLE PERMUTATIONS

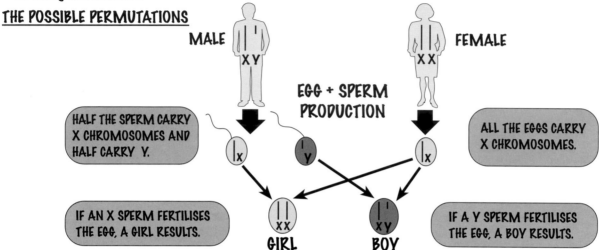

- Like all pairs of chromosomes, the SEX CHROMOSOMES SEPARATE DURING EGG + SPERM PRODUCTION ...
- ... (ie. meiosis) resulting in just one in each sperm or egg.

Ultimately, therefore, the sex of an individual is decided by whether the ovum is fertilised by an X-carrying sperm or a Y-carrying sperm.

Secondary Sexual Characteristics

Between the ages of 10 and 16 in girls, and 12 and 17 in boys, the ovaries (in girls!) and the testes (in boys!) begin to produce the hormones OESTROGEN and TESTOSTERONE which cause the development of the SECONDARY SEXUAL CHARACTERISTICS (PUBERTY).

GIRL	SEX	BOY
OESTROGEN	HORMONE	TESTOSTERONE
OVARIES	ENDOCRINE GLAND	TESTES
• OVULATION AND MENSTRUATION STARTS (ie. PERIODS). • GROWTH OF BREASTS, UTERUS & PELVIS. • GROWTH OF PUBIC HAIR AND ARMPIT HAIR. • DEVELOPMENT OF SOFTER, ROUNDER SHAPE. • FEELINGS OF ATTRACTION TO THE OPPOSITE SEX.	EFFECT ON TARGET ORGANS ie. DEVELOPMENT OF SECONDARY SEXUAL CHARACTERISTICS.	• PRODUCTION OF SPERM. • GROWTH OF MUSCLES AND PENIS. • VOICE BECOMES DEEPER. • BROADENING OF SHOULDERS. • GROWTH OF PUBIC HAIR, FACIAL HAIR AND BODY HAIR. • FEELINGS OF ATTRACTION TO THE OPPOSITE SEX.

The Menstrual Cycle

Between the ages of approximately 13 and 50, a woman is fertile and the lining of her uterus is replaced every month. This is a PERIOD. We can represent the changes in the uterus wall, the ovary and the level of hormones over the 28 day cycle like this ...

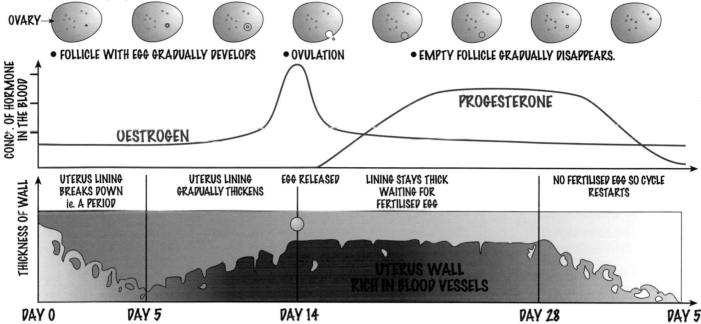

OVARY →

● FOLLICLE WITH EGG GRADUALLY DEVELOPS ● OVULATION ● EMPTY FOLLICLE GRADUALLY DISAPPEARS.

CONC^. OF HORMONE IN THE BLOOD

PROGESTERONE

OESTROGEN

THICKNESS OF WALL

| UTERUS LINING BREAKS DOWN ie. A PERIOD | UTERUS LINING GRADUALLY THICKENS | EGG RELEASED | LINING STAYS THICK WAITING FOR FERTILISED EGG | NO FERTILISED EGG SO CYCLE RESTARTS |

UTERUS WALL RICH IN BLOOD VESSELS

DAY 0   DAY 5   DAY 14   DAY 28   DAY 5

- OESTROGEN is produced by the OVARIES and causes the lining of the uterus to thicken during the early part of the menstrual cycle ie. it repairs it after a 'period'.
- PROGESTERONE is produced by the empty follicle in the ovary ('the yellow body') and preserves and maintains the uterus wall during the middle part of the cycle.
- If FERTILISATION occurs and a woman becomes pregnant then the empty follicle continues to produce progesterone until the placenta is formed. The placenta then continues to produce progesterone for the remainder of the pregnancy so maintaining the uterus wall and preventing further ovulation.

Natural Control Of Fertility

- Oestrogen and progesterone can be used to regulate the menstrual cycle in order to promote regular ovulation. This would then increase the chances of conception (fertilisation).
- Two hormones from the pituitary gland, F.S.H. and L.H., play a large role in the natural control of fertility.
- The diagram explains this, although you don't have to remember the specific hormones!

BRAIN

F.S.H. FROM PITUITARY CAUSES OVARIES TO PRODUCE OESTROGEN, AND AN EGG TO MATURE

L.H. ALSO FROM PITUITARY GLAND STIMULATES RELEASE OF EGG, IN MIDDLE OF MENSTRUAL CYCLE

PITUITARY

UTERUS

OVARY   OVARY

Artificial Control Of Fertility

- F.S.H. can be manufactured and given to women to help increase their fertility ...

F.S.H. ⟹
- Given as a FERTILITY DRUG ...
- ... to women who don't produce enough of it ...
- ... to stimulate eggs to mature and be released.

However, there is a very real risk of multiple births due to difficulties in administering exactly the right dose for each particular person.

Genes, Chromosomes And DNA

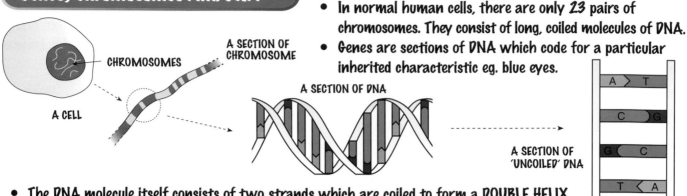

CHROMOSOMES

A CELL

A SECTION OF CHROMOSOME

A SECTION OF DNA

A SECTION OF 'UNCOILED' DNA

A > T
C > G
G > C
T < A

- In normal human cells, there are only **23** pairs of chromosomes. They consist of long, coiled molecules of DNA.
- Genes are sections of DNA which code for a particular inherited characteristic eg. blue eyes.

- The DNA molecule itself consists of two strands which are coiled to form a **DOUBLE HELIX**.
- The strands are linked by a series of **PAIRED BASES**: adenine, cytosine, guanine, and thymine (A,C,G and T).
- Adenine is only ever linked to thymine, **A – T**.
- Cytosine is only ever linked to guanine, **C – G**.

How Genes Work

- The DNA molecules form a complete set of instructions on how an organism should be 'constructed' and how that particular organism's cells should work.
- The instructions are in the form of a code, made up of the four bases which hold the strands of the molecule together. These bases are the important bit as they represent the order in which amino acids should be assembled to make proteins by living cells. Each group of three bases represent one amino acid in a protein chain.
- Since there are only about 20 amino acids, the code contained in the four bases is quite sufficient.

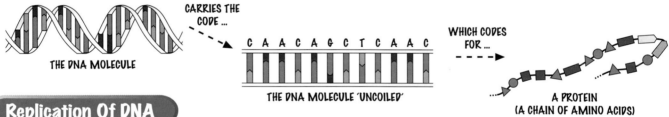

THE DNA MOLECULE

CARRIES THE CODE ...

C A A C A G C T C A A C

THE DNA MOLECULE 'UNCOILED'

WHICH CODES FOR ...

A PROTEIN (A CHAIN OF AMINO ACIDS)

Replication Of DNA

During cell division chromosomes make copies of themselves. In order to do this they must replicate their DNA, and this involves uncoiling it into separate strands.

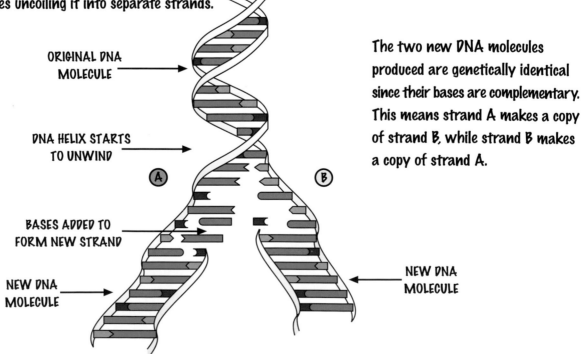

ORIGINAL DNA MOLECULE

DNA HELIX STARTS TO UNWIND

(A)   (B)

BASES ADDED TO FORM NEW STRAND

NEW DNA MOLECULE

NEW DNA MOLECULE

The two new DNA molecules produced are genetically identical since their bases are complementary. This means strand A makes a copy of strand B, while strand B makes a copy of strand A.

There are several long words associated with genetics, but don't be put off. The more you use them, the more familiar they will become to you. Here they are ...

ALLELE   This is an ALTERNATIVE FORM of a gene. So, for instance, if we were talking about genes for eye colour, we would say that there were two alleles for eye colour, brown and blue. Similarly the genes for being able/not able to roll your tongue are alleles.

DOMINANT   This refers to an allele which controls the development of a characteristic when it is present on only one of the chromosomes in a pair.

RECESSIVE   This refers to an allele which controls the development of a characteristic only if it is present on both of the chromosomes in a pair.

FOR EXAMPLE   It's perhaps a little easier to understand if we look at a diagram of a ...
... pair of chromosomes and specifically at genes which code for ...
... eye colour, tongue-rolling ability, and type of ear lobe.

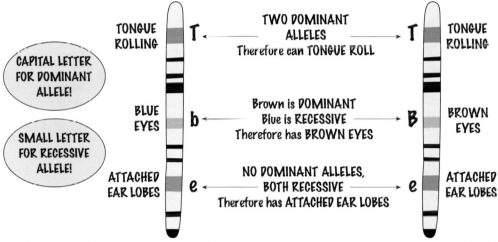

HIGHER TIER

- DOMINANT ALLELES EXPRESS THEMSELVES IF PRESENT ONLY ONCE ...
  ... so an individual can be HOMOZYGOUS DOMINANT (BB) or HETEROZYGOUS (Bb) for brown eyes.
- RECESSIVE ALLELES EXPRESS THEMSELVES ONLY IF PRESENT TWICE ...
  ... so an individual can only be HOMOZYGOUS RECESSIVE (bb) for blue eyes.

So the possible combinations are ...

	HOMOZYGOUS DOMINANT	HETEROZYGOUS	HOMOZYGOUS RECESSIVE
TONGUE ROLLING	TT (can roll)	Tt (can roll)	tt (can't roll)
EYE COLOUR	BB (brown)	Bb (brown)	bb (blue)
EAR LOBES	EE (free lobes)	Ee (free lobes)	ee (attached lobes)

HOMOZYGOUS   If both chromosomes in a pair contain the same allele of a gene then the individual is homozygous for that gene or condition.

HETEROZYGOUS   If the chromosomes in a pair contain different alleles of a gene then the individual is heterozygous for that gene or condition.

GENOTYPE   This refers to the particular pair of alleles representing a certain characteristic eg. we can refer to a homozygous dominant (BB) a homozygous recessive (bb) or a heterozygous (Bb) genotype for eye colour.

PHENOTYPE   This refers to the outward expression of a genotype (ie. what it actually produces!) eg. BB and Bb above are two different genotypes but each produces a brown-eyed phenotype. Only bb gives a blue-eyed phenotype.

Monohybrid Inheritance - An Explanation.

As we saw on the previous page, genes exist in pairs in diploid cells; one on each of a pair of chromosomes. We call these pairs of genes alleles when they code for alternatives of the same characteristic eg. eye colour. When a characteristic is determined by just one pair of alleles then simple genetic crosses can be performed to investigate the mechanism of inheritance. These simple crosses are examples of monohybrid inheritance.

Inheritance Of Eye Colour

In genetic diagrams we use CAPITAL LETTERS FOR DOMINANT ALLELES and LOWER CASE FOR RECESSIVE ALLELES. In eye colour therefore we use B for brown eye alleles and b for blue eye alleles ...

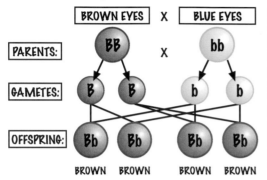
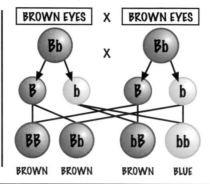
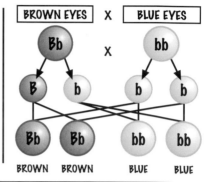

These are the typical examples you may be asked about in your exam. REMEMBER ...
to clearly identify the alleles of the parents ...
to place each of these alleles in a separate gamete ...
and then join each gamete with the two gametes from the OTHER PARENT!!

From the crosses above it can be seen that ...

... if one parent has 2 dominant genes then all the offspring will inherit that characteristic.

... if both parents have 1 recessive gene then this characteristic may appear in the offspring (a 1 in 4 chance).

... if one parent has a recessive gene and the other has 2, then there's a 50% chance of that characteristic appearing. But remember, these are only probabilities. In practice, all that matters is which egg is fertilised by which sperm!

HIGHER TIER

More Advanced Genetics Problems

These usually involve 'wordy' descriptions which you have to translate into crosses.

EXAMPLE 1 Draw genetic diagrams to predict the probable phenotypic ratios produced when two heterozygous brown eyed people mate.
Brown eyes are dominant to blue eyes.
A The genetic diagram reveals a 3:1 ratio of brown eyes to blue eyes.

EXAMPLE 2 In mice, white fur is dominant. What ratio of genotypes would you expect to be produced from a cross between a heterozygous individual and one with grey fur? Support your answer with a genetic diagram.
A There is a 1:1 ratio of heterozygous individuals to homozygous recessive individuals.

EXAMPLE 3 A homozygous long tailed cat is crossed with a homozygous short tailed cat and produces a litter of 9 long tailed kittens. Show the probable phenotypes which would be produced if two of these kittens were mated, and describe using genetic terminology the genotypes of the offspring.

A The phenotype ratio would be 3:1 in favour of long tails. There would be a $1/4$ chance of a homozygous dominant individual, a $2/4$ chance of a heterozygous individual and $1/4$ chance of a homozygous recessive individual.

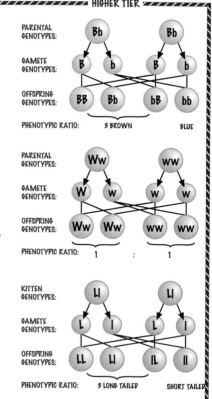

Reasons For Genetic Modification Of Organisms

Altering the genetic make-up of an organism can be done for many reasons ...

- To improve the crop yield eg. to produce larger tomatoes, potatoes, wheat seed-heads, more oil from oilseed rape etc etc etc.
- To improve resistance to pests or herbicides eg. Pyrethrum is an insecticide prepared from chrysanthemum plants. The actual gene for Pyrethrum can be inserted into soya plants to provide 'in-built' protection against insect damage.
- To extend the shelf-life of fast ripening crops such as tomatoes.
- To harness the cell chemistry of an organism so that it produces a substance that you require, eg. production of human insulin.

All these processes involve transferring genetic material from one organism to another in order to give the recipient organism some sort of benefit. The recipient organism must then reproduce asexually in order to pass on its new genetic make-up to its offspring.

HIGHER TIER

Genetic Engineering - The Process

Human insulin can be produced by genetic engineering. This is a hormone, produced by the pancreas, which helps to control the level of glucose in the blood. Diabetics can't produce enough insulin and often need to inject it.

STEP 1

PART OF A HUMAN CHROMOSOME

HUMAN INSULIN GENE

INSULIN GENE 'CUT OUT'

The gene for insulin production is 'cut out' of a human chromosome using RESTRICTION ENZYMES.
These 'cut' DNA at very specific places enabling scientists to remove the precise piece of DNA they want; in this case the gene for insulin production.

STEP 2

Another restriction enzyme is then used to cut open a ring of bacterial DNA (a plasmid). Other enzymes are then used to insert the piece of human DNA into the plasmid. The repaired plasmid is now ready for step 3.

RING OF BACTERIAL DNA CUT OPEN

HUMAN INSULIN GENE INSERTED INTO BACTERIAL DNA

STEP 3

VAT

The plasmid is now reinserted into a bacterium which starts to divide rapidly. As it divides it replicates the plasmid and soon there are millions of them - each with instructions to make insulin.

- When the above process has been completed the bacteria is CULTURED ON A LARGE SCALE ...
- ... and COMMERCIAL QUANTITIES OF INSULIN are then produced.

The Great Genetics Debate

- SCIENTISTS have made GREAT ADVANCES in their understanding of genes and ...
1. ... have IDENTIFIED GENES that control certain characteristics.
2. ... can determine whether a person's genes may lead to them having an INCREASED RISK of CONTRACTING A PARTICULAR ILLNESS eg. breast cancer.
3. ... may soon be able to 'REMOVE' FAULTY GENES and reduce genetic diseases.

- Some parts of society are CONCERNED that ...
1. ... unborn children will be GENETICALLY SCREENED and aborted if their genetic make-up is faulty.
2. ... parents may want to artificially DECIDE ON THE GENETIC MAKE-UP of their child.
3. ... some insurance companies may GENETICALLY SCREEN applicants and refuse to insure people who have an increased genetic risk of an illness or disease. This may prevent these people being able to drive or buy homes due to lack of insurance.

How Mutations Affect DNA Structure

Mutations are changes to the structure of the D.N.A. molecule which result in a new form of gene.

These changes can then be passed onto 'daughter' cells as a result of cell division.

In other words the organisation of part of the D.N.A. molecule is somehow disturbed resulting in ...

... the cell producing different sequences of amino acids and therefore different proteins!

A GENE 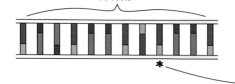 GENE NOW ALTERED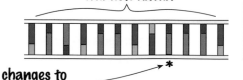

changes to

This can change the entire nature of the particular gene.

CAUSES	EFFECTS
• Mutations occur naturally but ...	• Most mutations are HARMFUL and in ...
• .... there is an increased risk of mutation if ...	• ... REPRODUCTIVE CELLS can cause DEATH or ABNORMALITY.
• ... individuals are exposed to MUTAGENIC AGENTS ...	• In BODY CELLS they may cause CANCER.
• ... e.g. IONISING RADIATION (Inc. U-V LIGHT, X-RAYS) ...	• Some mutations are NEUTRAL, and in RARE CASES ...
• ... RADIOACTIVE SUBSTANCES and CERTAIN CHEMICALS.	• ... may INCREASE THE SURVIVAL CHANCES OF AN ORGANISM, ...
• THE GREATER THE DOSE, THE GREATER THE RISK.	• ... and its OFFSPRING WHO INHERIT THE GENE.

Penicillin-Resistant Bacteria

This is an increasing problem and is caused by a mutation in the bacteria which confers resistance to penicillin. Consequently non-resistant bacteria are killed off leaving the field free for the resistant ones to reproduce passing on their resistance. This is why Doctors are reluctant to prescribe antibiotics when the patient can do without them.

The Human Genome Project

A man called Sanger discovered a way of sequencing the bases in DNA in 1977 (see P.20) and subsequently (in 1986) the project was initiated to produce the first map of the human genome ie. discover where all 30,000 genes were and what they did! The completed map is due to be published soon.

THE DIFFICULTIES

Dominant genes which controlled a particular characteristic were relatively easy to map. Recessive alleles were harder to find because they were often masked. Harder still were those features that are controlled by several genes acting together.

THE ISSUES

You could map the genome of an individual and find out what he's likely to develop as an illness or disability!

Yes but imagine knowing what might happen to you even though there's a strong chance that it never will.

If everyone knew their genome, lots of people would realise they were going to have quite a nice life.

Lots of people would be regarded as inferior by supposedly superior people with a 'better' genome.

But wouldn't it be good to know that you possess a gene which made it unlikely that you would ever get lung cancer?

What about those who didn't have the gene? How do you think Insurance Companies might view them? As an unacceptable risk?

Well at least 'nasty' genes might one day be able to be removed from embryos so that the baby will be born healthy.

But suppose Doctors start to offer people 'Designer Babies' with characteristics of their choosing. How scary would that be?

Preventing genetic diseases and finding better medicines must surely be a good thing?

Well, yes, I agree but can we afford to pay the price of all the other things that might happen? It's a tough choice.

- ADAPTATIONS are SPECIAL FEATURES OR BEHAVIOUR which make an organism...
  ...ESPECIALLY WELL SUITED TO ITS ENVIRONMENT.

- ADAPTATIONS are part of the EVOLUTIONARY PROCESS which 'shapes life' so that a habitat is populated by organisms which excel there. Adaptations increase an organism's chance of survival; they are 'biological solutions' to an environmental challenge!

Examples Of How Organisms Are Adapted To Their Environment

... LIFE IN A VERY COLD CLIMATE - THE POLAR BEAR

- SMALL SURFACE AREA/VOLUME RATIO to REDUCE HEAT LOSS.
- LARGE AMOUNT OF INSULATING FAT beneath the skin.
- WHITE COAT so that it is CAMOUFLAGED.
- LARGE FEET to spread its weight on the ice.
- POWERFUL SWIMMER so that it can CATCH ITS FOOD.
- HIBERNATES in the worst weather.

... LIFE IN A VERY HOT CLIMATE - THE CAMEL

- LARGE SURFACE AREA/VOLUME RATIO to INCREASE HEAT LOSS.
- BODY FAT STORED IN HUMP with almost none beneath the skin.
- SANDY BROWN COAT to CAMOUFLAGE it in the desert.
- LOSES VERY LITTLE WATER through sweating or in urine.
- CAN DRINK UP TO 20 GALLONS OF WATER in one go.

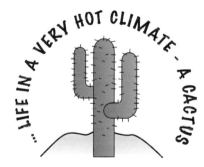
... LIFE IN A VERY HOT CLIMATE - A CACTUS

- SMALL SURFACE AREA/VOLUME RATIO to REDUCE WATER LOSS.
- THICK, WAXY SURFACE to REDUCE WATER LOSS.
- STORES WATER in spongy layer inside its stem.
- SPINES PROTECT THE CACTI from predators who would 'steal' the CACTI'S WATER STORE.
- STOMATA ONLY OPEN AT NIGHT to REDUCE THE AMOUNT OF WATER LOST compared to daytime.
- Some cacti have SHALLOW SPREADING ROOTS ...
  ... to ABSORB SURFACE WATER whilst others have ...
  ... DEEP ROOTS to tap into underground supplies of water.

... LIFE IN AN AQUATIC (WATERY) ENVIRONMENT - THE FISH

- Fish are STREAMLINED in shape to allow them to TRAVEL QUICKLY through the water.
- They possess GILLS that can obtain DISSOLVED OXYGEN FROM THE WATER.
- GILLS have a LARGE SURFACE AREA which INCREASE THE AREA over which OXYGEN CAN BE ABSORBED.

Competition

Organisms compete with each other for ...

Plants need light and room to spread leaves.	⟵ **SPACE** ⟶	Animals need space to breed and 'rest'. Also territory to hunt in.
Plants absorb nutrients from the soil.	⟵ **FOOD** ⟶	Herbivores compete for vegetation, and carnivores compete for their prey.
All plants must absorb water by their roots.	⟵ **WATER** ⟶	All animals need water in order to survive.

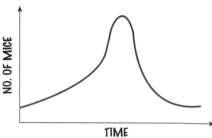

Even if there is ample food and water, an increasing population will eventually reach a size when overcrowding, disease and aggression will cause stress within the population leading to a dramatic fall in numbers. The graph shows an experiment where mice were given surplus food and water everyday with dead mice being removed. The mice were contained within a closed barn.

- When two or more organisms compete in a particular area or habitat, the ORGANISMS WHICH ARE BETTER ADAPTED TO THE ENVIRONMENT ARE MORE SUCCESSFUL and usually exist in larger numbers - often resulting in the complete exclusion of the other competing organisms.

In your examination you may be asked to suggest the factors for which organisms are competing in a given habitat.

Predator/Prey Cycles

- PREDATORS are ANIMALS that KILL and EAT OTHER ANIMALS while ...
- ... the ANIMALS that are EATEN are called the PREY.
- Within a NATURAL ENVIRONMENT there is a DELICATE BALANCE ...
- ... between the POPULATION of the PREDATOR and its PREY.

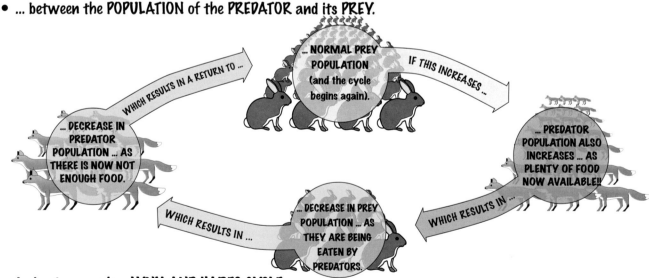

A classic example - LYNX AND HARES CYCLE

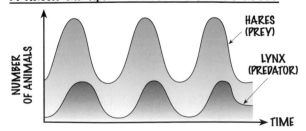

- Over a period of time the POPULATION of ...
- ... LYNX and HARES does a FULL CYCLE.
- There are always more ...
- ... HARES than LYNX while ...
- ... the POPULATION PEAK for the LYNX always comes ...
- ... AFTER the POPULATION PEAK for the HARES.

N.B. THE ABOVE GRAPH WOULD BE VERY SIMILAR FOR ANY PREDATOR AND PREY POPULATION CYCLE.

Charles Darwin

He made four very important observations ...
- All living things produce far more offspring than actually survive to adulthood.
- In spite of this, population sizes remain fairly constant, all things being equal.
- There is variation in members of the same species.
- Characteristics can be passed on from one generation to the next.

From these observations Darwin deduced that all organisms were involved in a struggle for survival in which only the best adapted organisms would survive, reproduce and pass on their characteristics. This formed the basis for his famous theory of 'Evolution by Natural Selection'.

Evolution By Natural Selection

Evolution is the CHANGE IN A POPULATION over a large number of generations that may result in THE FORMATION OF A NEW SPECIES; the members of which are BETTER ADAPTED TO THEIR ENVIRONMENT.

There are 4 key points to remember:-

1. Individuals within a population show VARIATION (ie. differences due to their genes).
2. There is COMPETITION between individuals for food and mates etc., and also predation and disease. This keeps population sizes constant in spite of the production of many offspring, i.e. there is a 'struggle for survival', and many individuals die.
3. Individuals which are BETTER ADAPTED to the environment are more likely to survive, breed successfully and produce offspring. This is termed 'SURVIVAL OF THE FITTEST'.
4. These 'survivors' will therefore PASS ON THEIR GENES to these offspring resulting in an improved organism being evolved through NATURAL SELECTION.

VARIATION and COMPETITION ensure BETTER ADAPTED organisms PASS ON THEIR GENES

The Peppered Moth

The Peppered Moth is a PALE COLOUR and...
...was ADAPTED TO ITS ENVIRONMENT.
The moth was CAMOUFLAGED against silver birch trees
and the BIRDS THAT ATE the moth found it DIFFICULT to see them.

During the INDUSTRIAL REVOLUTION the air became more POLLUTED
and the silver birch trees started to get very sooty.

VARIATION
- Following the INDUSTRIAL REVOLUTION a new variety of DARK-COLOURED MOTH appeared.
- The dark colour was probably due to a GENETIC MUTATION.

COMPETITION
- The WELL-CAMOUFLAGED DARK-COLOURED MOTH was eaten LESS OFTEN than the PALE-COLOURED MOTH, because the birds couldn't see it so easily.

BETTER ADAPTED
- The DARK-COLOURED MOTH SURVIVED LONGER and was able to BREED MORE OFTEN, because it now had a significant advantage.

PASS ON THEIR GENES
- The DARK-COLOURED MOTHS PASSED ON THEIR GENES MORE OFTEN and many more DARK-COLOURED Peppered Moths are found in areas where the air is polluted.

The Clean Air Act

The Clean Air Act of the 1950's reduced air-borne pollution dramatically over the next ten years or so; the new generation of silver birches actually stayed 'silver'.
This meant that the pale variety once again had an advantage and due to natural selection began to become more common again. The presence of the pale variety is now regarded as a marker for pollution-free air.

The Theory Of Evolution

The THEORY OF EVOLUTION states...

...that all LIVING THINGS which EXIST TODAY and many more that are now EXTINCT...

...have EVOLVED from simple life forms, which first developed 3,000,000,000 (billion) years ago.

- EVOLUTION is the SLOW, CONTINUAL CHANGE of organisms over a VERY LONG PERIOD...
  ...to become BETTER ADAPTED to their environment.
- If the ENVIRONMENT CHANGES, SPECIES MUST CHANGE with it if they are TO SURVIVE.
- Species which AREN'T ADAPTED to their environment will become EXTINCT.
- A SPECIES is defined as a group of organisms which can freely interbreed to produce FERTILE offspring.

The Reasons For Extinction Of Species

INCREASED COMPETITION

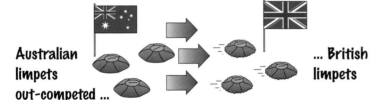

Australian limpets out-competed ...

... British limpets

CHANGE IN THE ENVIRONMENT

ONCE WELL ADAPTED   NOW POORLY ADAPTED

NEW PREDATORS

The Dodo ... hunted by humans and animals introduced by humans.

NEW DISEASES

The Fossil Record

FOSSILS are the 'REMAINS' of PLANTS OR ANIMALS from many years ago...
...which are FOUND IN ROCK.

The FOSSIL RECORD is INCOMPLETE because...

1. ...some BODY PARTS may NOT BE FOSSILISED

2. ...some fossils have NOT YET BEEN DISCOVERED

3. ...FOSSILISATION RARELY OCCURS because MICROBES DECAY the organic material that makes up living things.

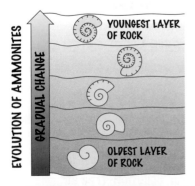

EVOLUTION OF AMMONITES — GRADUAL CHANGE

YOUNGEST LAYER OF ROCK

OLDEST LAYER OF ROCK

- If we look at exposed rock strata, ...
- ... it is possible to follow the GRADUAL CHANGES which have taken place in an organism over time.
- Even though the fossil record is incomplete, these gradual changes confirm that ...
- ... SPECIES HAVE CHANGED OVER LONG PERIODS OF TIME ...
- ... providing <u>STRONG EVIDENCE FOR EVOLUTION.</u>

Selective Breeding Down The Ages

Farmers and livestock have been using the principles of selective breeding for hundreds of years without really understanding the genetic basis for it. The simple rule was to keep the best examples of your animals and plants for breeding and to take the rest to market. The same is true of dog breeders who have systematically selected animals which show the desired characteristics and bred them ...

Choose the two spottiest to breed ... and then the spottiest of their offspring ...   to eventually get Dalmations.

Development Of Modern Cattle

In a competitive farming industry, cattle need to be highly efficient at their job if the farm is to make money. Efficiency means specialisation. In other words cattle have been carefully bred to fulfil certain criteria. In general, this means cattle are selectively bred for one of the following characteristics ...

- **QUANTITY OF MILK PRODUCED ...**
  Some cattle are milk specialists. They churn the stuff out at a great rate and we're all very happy about that. This is no coincidence. These are the result of years of breeding good milk producers with other good milk producers to end up with the champions we have now.

Friesian

- **QUALITY OF MILK PRODUCED ...**
  The amount of fat in milk is a sign of its quality and some cows, although perhaps not producing the same volume as other cows, produce lovely creamy, high fat milk. Again, this is down to artificial selection.

Jersey

- **BEEF PRODUCTION ...**
  The characteristics of the Hereford and Angus varieties have been selected over the past 200 years. They include hardiness, early maturity, high numbers of offspring, and the swift efficient conversion of grass into meat.

Hereford

Increasing Number Of Offspring In Sheep

Sheep which produce twins are extremely desirable animals since there are obviously twice as many animals to take to market. Producing twins is an inherited trait ie some animals are more prone to it than others. Consequently this characteristic is selected by breeders.

Increasing Yield From Dwarf Wheat

Dwarf wheat plants are sturdier, and put less energy into the growth of their stems (the bit that eventually becomes straw). Consequently, wheat can be bred to produce high yielding seed-heads on a dwarf plant to maximise cost- effectiveness.

Reasons For Pollution

Pollution is the contamination of the environment by waste substances, many of which are formed as a result of burning fossil fuels for energy production. The biggest culprits in all of this are the industrialised democracies of the Western World. Needless to say they have some of the highest densities of population.

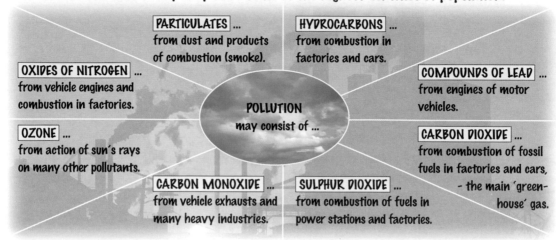

PARTICULATES ... from dust and products of combustion (smoke).

HYDROCARBONS ... from combustion in factories and cars.

OXIDES OF NITROGEN ... from vehicle engines and combustion in factories.

COMPOUNDS OF LEAD ... from engines of motor vehicles.

OZONE ... from action of sun's rays on many other pollutants.

POLLUTION may consist of ...

CARBON DIOXIDE ... from combustion of fossil fuels in factories and cars, - the main 'greenhouse' gas.

CARBON MONOXIDE ... from vehicle exhausts and many heavy industries.

SULPHUR DIOXIDE ... from combustion of fuels in power stations and factories.

The Effects Of Sulphur Dioxide

Sulphur dioxide is a choking, irritant gas with a very pungent smell. It dissolves in water to form sulphurous acid, (similar to sulphuric acid). It has the following effects ...

- It dissolves in the moist lining of the lungs causing irritation and violent coughing. The results of persistent coughing can damage the air sacs causing **EMPHYSEMA**. Irritation can also cause **ASTHMA**.
- It dissolves in water vapour to form acid rain which ...
  - corrodes stone and metal in buildings
  - raises the acidity of lakes and streams, damaging wildlife.
  - 'burns out' the growing tips of trees.

Acid rain has become an increasing problem since the industrial revolution due to the increasing use of fossil fuels containing sulphur as an impurity.

Vehicle Exhaust Gases

Some of the harmful substances occurring in exhaust gases from vehicles include ...
- **OXIDES OF NITROGEN** • **CARBON MONOXIDE** • **CARBON DIOXIDE**

However carbon dioxide is a natural constituent of the air, it makes up about 0.03%.

Increasing levels of CO_2 result in global warming due to the 'greenhouse effect'. The other two types of pollutant are actually poisonous gases and need to be eliminated, or at least reduced. Ways of doing this are as follows ...

CARBON MONOXIDE	• Use of more efficient engines which completely burn the fuel. • Catalytic converters to convert carbon monoxide to CO_2	
OXIDES OF NITROGEN	• Use a catalytic converter in which nitrogen monoxide combines with carbon monoxide to produce nitrogen and carbon dioxide.	

Other ways of reducing the problem caused by pollution from cars include ...

Using alternative fuels

Using more public transport

Providing more traffic free zones

Reducing speed limits

Increasing the price of fuel and road tax.

VARIATION, CELL DIVISION AND D.N.A

VARIATION describes differences between individuals of the same species, and is due to a combination of GENETIC AND ENVIRONMENTAL CAUSES.
• SEXUAL Reproduction causes lots of variation.
• ASEXUAL Reproduction causes no variation (ie. clones)

CELL DIVISION

MEIOSIS (Haploid Cells) ← → MITOSIS (Diploid Cells)

• MEIOSIS - Reproductive cell division which halves the chromosome number.
• MITOSIS - Normal cell division which maintains the number of chromosomes.

THE NATURE OF THE GENE
• A gene is a section of DNA which determines a particular inherited characteristic eg. blue eyes.
• The strands of the double helix are linked by 4 bases, ... ADENINE linked to THYMINE, ... and CYTOSINE to GUANINE.
• The instructions in the DNA are in the form of a code made of the 4 bases.
• A code of 3 bases represents 1 amino acid.
• During cell division chromosomes make copies of themselves, and must therefore replicate their DNA by making a complementary copy.

INHERITANCE OF SEX, SEX HORMONES AND MENSTRUAL CYCLE

INHERITANCE OF SEX
This is determined by the X and Y chromosomes.
Whichever type of sperm fertilisers the egg decides the sex.

SECONDARY SEXUAL CHARACTERISTICS

	GIRL	SEX	BOY
	OESTROGEN	HORMONE	TESTOSTERONE
	OVARIES	ENDOCRINE GLAND	TESTES
	• OVULATION AND MENSTRUATION STARTS (ie. PERIODS). • GROWTH OF BREASTS, UTERUS & PELVIS. • GROWTH OF PUBIC HAIR AND ARMPIT HAIR. • DEVELOPMENT OF SOFTER, ROUNDER SHAPE. • FEELINGS OF ATTRACTION TO THE OPPOSITE SEX.	EFFECT ON TARGET ORGANS ie. DEVELOPMENT OF SECONDARY SEXUAL CHARACTERISTICS.	• PRODUCTION OF SPERM. • GROWTH OF MUSCLES AND PENIS. • VOICE BECOMES DEEPER. • BROADENING OF SHOULDERS. • GROWTH OF PUBIC HAIR, FACIAL HAIR AND BODY HAIR. • FEELINGS OF ATTRACTION TO THE OPPOSITE SEX.

THE MENSTRUAL CYCLE

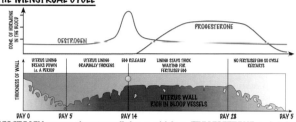

OESTROGEN causes the uterus lining to thicken, PROGESTERONE maintains it.
• Manufactured sex hormone (F.S.H) can be given to stimulate fertility

MONOHYBRID INHERITANCE AND TERMINOLOGY

• ALLELES - Alternative forms of genes eg. blue and brown eyes.
• DOMINANT - An allele which expresses itself when present on only one of the chromosomes of a pair.
• RECESSIVE - An allele which expresses itself only when present on both chromosomes of a pair.

• In this example, Brown eyes are dominant to blue eyes and so all the offspring have brown eyes in this particular cross.

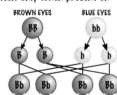

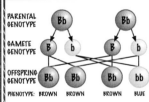

PARENTAL GENOTYPE / GAMETE GENOTYPE / OFFSPRING GENOTYPE / PHENOTYPE: BROWN BROWN BROWN BLUE

• HOMOZYGOUS -Both chromosomes of the pair contain the SAME allele.
• HETEROZYGOUS - the chromosomes in the pair contain different alleles.
• GENOTYPE - The description of the actual alleles carried by an individual for a certain characteristic. ie. BB-Homozygous dominant, Bb-Heterozygous, and bb-Homozygous recessive.
• PHENOTYPE - The outward expression of a genotype eg. blue eyes.

CHANGING AND MAPPING GENES

GENETIC ENGINEERING

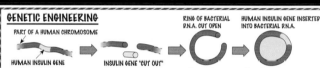

PART OF A HUMAN CHROMOSOME / HUMAN INSULIN GENE / INSULIN GENE "CUT OUT" / RING OF BACTERIAL D.N.A. CUT OPEN / HUMAN INSULIN GENE INSERTED INTO BACTERIAL D.N.A.

• Restriction enzymes are used to cut and place the gene. In this case human insulin is manufactured.

MUTATIONS are changes to the structure of the DNA molecule which results in a new form of gene.

CAUSES	EFFECTS
• Mutations occur naturally but ... • .... there is an increased risk of mutation if ... • ... individuals are exposed to MUTAGENIC AGENTS ... • ... e.g. IONISING RADIATION (inc. U-V LIGHT, X-RAYS) ... • ... RADIOACTIVE SUBSTANCES and CERTAIN CHEMICALS. • ... THE GREATER THE DOSE, THE GREATER THE RISK.	• Most mutations are HARMFUL and in ... • ... REPRODUCTIVE CELLS can cause DEATH or ABNORMALITY. • In BODY CELLS they may cause CANCER. • Some mutations are NEUTRAL, and in RARE CASES ... • ... may INCREASE THE SURVIVAL CHANCES OF AN ORGANISM... • ... and its OFFSPRING WHO INHERIT THE GENE.

THE HUMAN GENOME PROJECT
All the genes on human chromosomes successfully mapped. Recessives and multiple genes proved the most difficult.

PROS
Information can help to predict and therefore prevent many illnesses and conditions, so benefiting the human race.

CONS
The information may be used to discriminate against people and also to manipulate the characteristics of unborn babies.

ADAPTATION, COMPETITION AND POLLUTION

ADAPTATIONS are special features or behaviour which make an organism well-suited to its environment. They are part of the evolutionary process -'a biological solution to an environmental challenge'. All organisms show such features.

COMPETITION Organisms compete for SPACE , FOOD and WATER.
When two or more organisms compete in a habitat, the ones which are BETTER ADAPTED ARE MORE SUCCESSFUL, and will eventually exist in larger numbers.

PREDATOR-PREY CYCLES
The population peak for the predator always comes after the peak for the prey.

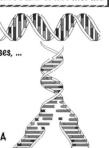

POLLUTION

PARTICULATES ... HYDROCARBONS ... / OXIDES OF NITROGEN / POLLUTION may consist of ... / OZONE ... / COMPOUNDS OF LEAD / CARBON DIOXIDE ... / CARBON MONOXIDE ... SULPHUR DIOXIDE ...

CARBON MONOXIDE	• Use of more efficient engines which completely burn the fuel. • Catalytic converters to convert carbon monoxide to CO_2.
OXIDES OF NITROGEN	• Use a catalytic converter in which nitrogen monoxide combines with carbon monoxide to produce nitrogen and carbon dioxide.

EVOLUTION AND ARTIFICIAL SELECTION

EVOLUTION BY NATURAL SELECTION
• In all populations there is VARIATION.
• There is always COMPETITION for food and mates and this keeps population sizes constant in spite of many offspring.
• The BETTER ADAPTED individuals will be able to produce the most offspring.
• These 'survivors' will PASS ON THEIR GENES which made them better adapted individuals, resulting in evolution.

REASONS FOR EXTINCTION
• INCREASED COMPETITION
• NEW PREDATORS
• CHANGE IN THE ENVIRONMENT
• NEW DISEASES
If an organism isn't well adapted it won't survive.
The fossil record, though incomplete, provides evidence for evolution by showing that species have changed over long periods of time.

ARTIFICIAL SELECTION or selective breeding means breeding the 'best' to the 'best' and retaining the 'best' offspring. This principle has been used to ...
• Increase the quality and quantity of milk produced by cattle.
• Increase the quality and quantity of beef.
• Increase the number of offspring in sheep (twinning).
• Increase the yield from dwarf wheat plants.

This page is similar to work covered in Module 6, but there are important differences.

Structure Of An Atom

Everything is made up of atoms. Atoms contain three types of particles: protons, neutrons (except hydrogen!) and electrons.

This is an atom of fluorine:

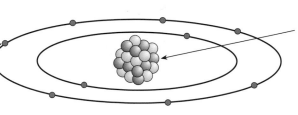

The nucleus is surrounded by orbiting electrons ● which are negatively charged and arranged in shells. A fluorine atom contains 9 electrons.

This is the nucleus. It contains protons ◐ which are positively charged and neutrons ◯ which are neutral.
The nucleus is small and heavy. A fluorine atom contains 9 protons and 10 neutrons.

ATOMIC PARTICLE		RELATIVE MASS	RELATIVE CHARGE
PROTON	◐	1	+1
NEUTRON	◯	1	0
ELECTRON	●	1/1840 (almost nothing)	-1

- An atom has the same number of protons as electrons, so the atom as a whole has no electrical charge.
- A proton has the same mass as a neutron.
- The mass of an electron is negligible ie. nearly nothing compared to a proton or neutron.

Here are three other atoms ...

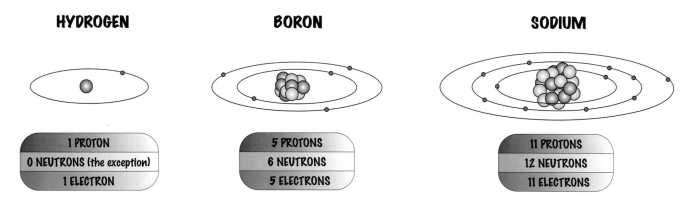

HYDROGEN

| 1 PROTON |
| 0 NEUTRONS (the exception) |
| 1 ELECTRON |

BORON

| 5 PROTONS |
| 6 NEUTRONS |
| 5 ELECTRONS |

SODIUM

| 11 PROTONS |
| 12 NEUTRONS |
| 11 ELECTRONS |

Atomic Number

The ATOMIC NUMBER of an element tells us the NUMBER OF PROTONS found in the nucleus of an atom of that element, for example ...

The atomic number ...
... of LITHIUM, Li, is 3.
Its nucleus contains 3 protons.

The atomic number ...
.... of NITROGEN, N, is 7.
Its nucleus contains 7 protons.

The atomic number ...
... of IRON, Fe, is 26.
Its nucleus contains 26 protons.

The Periodic Table

ELEMENTS are the 'building blocks' of all materials. The 100 or so elements are arranged in order of INCREASING ATOMIC NUMBER. The list can then be arranged in rows so that elements with similar properties are in the same column, or GROUP. This forms the basis of the PERIODIC TABLE ...

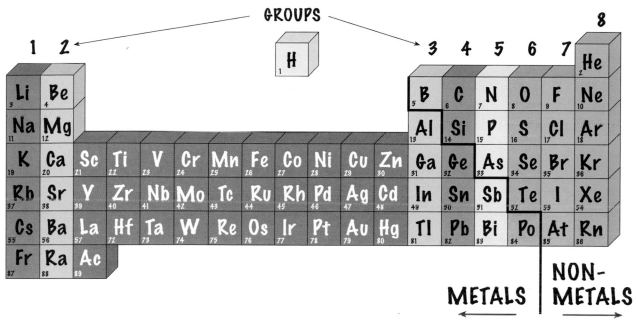

- More than ¾ of the elements are METALS.
- Metals are found mainly in Groups 1 and 2 and in the central block.
- Group 1 elements are known as the ALKALI METALS.
- Group 7 elements are known as the HALOGENS.
- Group 8 elements are known as the NOBLE GASES.

Trends In The Periodic Table

As we go down a particular group, elements have SIMILAR CHEMICAL PROPERTIES ...
... since they have the same number of electrons in their outermost shell (see next page).

- Elements in Group 1 (which all have 1 electron in their outermost shell) become MORE REACTIVE as we go down the group because the OUTERMOST ELECTRON SHELL gets further away from the influence of the nucleus and so electrons are MORE EASILY LOST.

- Elements in Group 7 (which all have 7 electrons in their outermost shell) become LESS REACTIVE as we go down the group because the OUTERMOST ELECTRON SHELL gets further away from the influence of the nucleus and so electrons are LESS EASILY GAINED.

- ELEMENTS IN GROUP 8 however, all have FULL OUTERMOST ELECTRON SHELLS and they do not need to lose or gain electrons in reactions to become stable and so they do not react with many other elements.

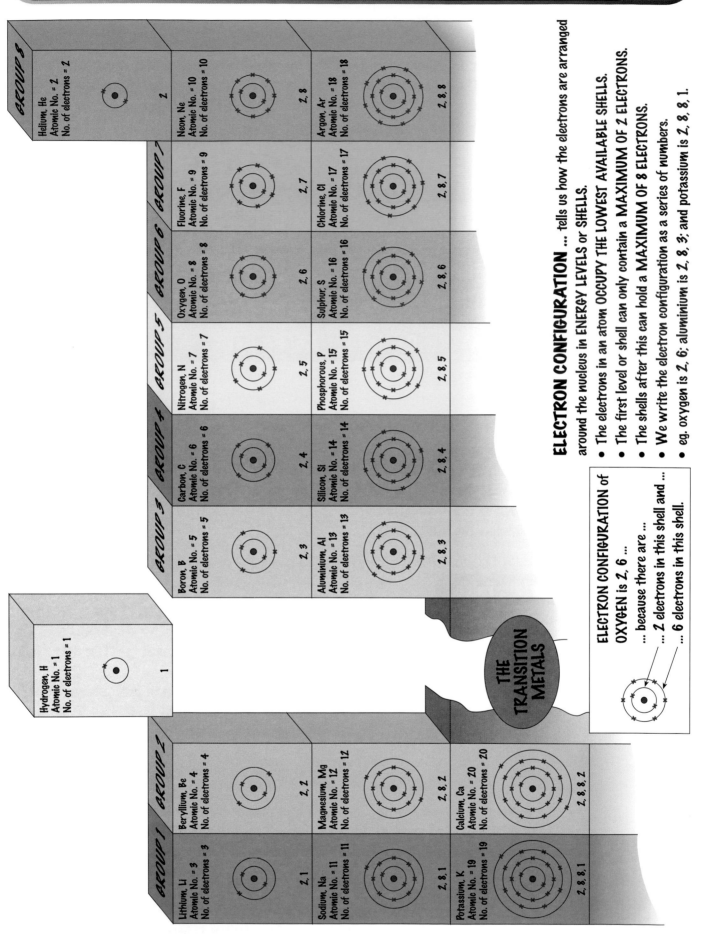

ELECTRON CONFIGURATION ... tells us how the electrons are arranged around the nucleus in ENERGY LEVELS or SHELLS.

- The electrons in an atom OCCUPY THE LOWEST AVAILABLE SHELLS.
- The first level or shell can only contain a MAXIMUM OF 2 ELECTRONS.
- The shells after this can hold a MAXIMUM OF 8 ELECTRONS.
- We write the electron configuration as a series of numbers.
- eg. oxygen is 2, 6; aluminium is 2, 8, 3; and potassium is 2, 8, 8, 1.

ELECTRON CONFIGURATION of OXYGEN is 2, 6 ...
... because there are ...
... 2 electrons in this shell and ...
... 6 electrons in this shell.

THE TRANSITION METALS

As you will notice there is a connection between the number of outer electrons and the position of an element in a group ie. elements in group 1 have 1 electron only in their outermost shell, elements in group 2 have 2 electrons only in their outermost shell and so on.

Group 7 - The Halogens

There are FIVE NON-METALS in this group ...
... but the top four are the ones we need to be concerned about.
They ALL VARY IN COLOUR, ...
... and their BOILING POINT INCREASES as we go down the group, ...
... which, along with their melting point, ...
... determines their physical state at room temperature.

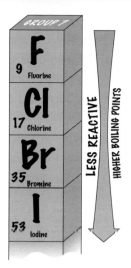

HALOGEN	FLUORINE	CHLORINE	BROMINE	IODINE
BOILING POINT (°C)	-188°C	-34°C	59°C (melting pt -7°C)	184°C (melting pt 114°C)
COLOUR & PHYSICAL STATE AT ROOM TEMP.	PALE YELLOW VAPOUR	PALE GREEN VAPOUR	RED-BROWN LIQUID	GREY SOLID

Reactions Of Chlorine With Sodium And Iron

• A piece of SODIUM is placed in a combustion spoon. The spoon is heated until the sodium just catches fire. The spoon is then immediately put into a gas jar of CHLORINE and placed in a fume cupboard.
The following reaction takes place ...

SODIUM + CHLORINE $\longrightarrow$ SODIUM CHLORIDE

$$2Na_{(s)} + Cl_{2(g)} \longrightarrow 2NaCl_{(s)}$$

• IRON, in the form of iron wool, is heated strongly and CHLORINE gas is passed over it in a fume cupboard.
The iron wool will glow brightly as the following reaction takes place ...

IRON + CHLORINE $\longrightarrow$ IRON (III) CHLORIDE

$$2Fe_{(s)} + 3Cl_{2(g)} \longrightarrow 2FeCl_{3(s)}$$

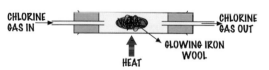

CHLORINE GAS IN   CHLORINE GAS OUT
GLOWING IRON WOOL
HEAT

Displacement Reactions Of The Halogens

The halogens' atomic numbers increase as we go down the group and they become less reactive.
This can be shown by the displacement reactions of halogens with solutions of other halides.

chlorine gas →

bromine being formed due to the displacement reaction

potassium bromide solution

In summary ...

Chlorine - Most reactive
Bromine
Iodine - Least reactive

	Potassium Chloride $KCl_{(aq)}$	Potassium Bromide $KBr_{(aq)}$	Potassium Iodide $KI_{(aq)}$
Chlorine Cl_2	✕	+ KCl Bromine	+ KCl Iodine
Bromine Br_2	No Reaction	✕	+ KBr Iodine
Iodine I_2	No Reaction	No Reaction	✕

Uses Of The Halogens

• IODINE solution is used as an antiseptic.
• CHLORINE is used in WATER PURIFICATION
eg. swimming pools and domestic water supplies, as it kills bacteria.
It is also used for BLEACHING paper, wood and cloth.

Chemical reactions only occur when **REACTING PARTICLES COLLIDE WITH EACH OTHER** with sufficient energy to react. The minimum amount of energy required to cause this reaction is called the **ACTIVATION ENERGY**. These reactions can proceed at different speeds ...
• **RUSTING** is a slow reaction • **BURNING** is a fast reaction.
There are **FOUR** important factors which affect the **RATE OF REACTION**:
TEMPERATURE, SURFACE AREA, CONCENTRATION and USE OF A CATALYST.

Temperature Of The Reactants

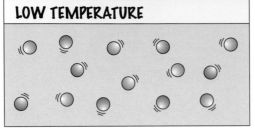

LOW TEMPERATURE

FASTER SPEED ...
... MORE COLLISIONS.

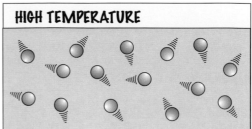

HIGH TEMPERATURE

In a COLD reaction mixture the particles are moving quite SLOWLY - the particles will collide with each other less often, with less energy, and less collisions will be successful.

CLOSE UP VIEW
REACTION RATE IS SLOW

If we HEAT the reaction mixture the particles will move more QUICKLY - the particles will collide with each other more often, with greater energy, and many more collisions will be successful.

CLOSE UP VIEW
REACTION RATE IS FASTER

Demonstration

If we add hydrochloric acid to sodium thiosulphate ...

HYDROCHLORIC ACID + SODIUM THIOSULPHATE ⟶ SODIUM CHLORIDE + SULPHUR + SULPHUR DIOXIDE + WATER

$$2HCl_{(aq)} + Na_2S_2O_{3(aq)} \longrightarrow 2NaCl_{(aq)} + S_{(s)} + SO_{2(g)} + H_2O_{(l)}$$

As the yellow sulphur precipitate is produced the solution becomes cloudy. We can measure the rate of the reaction by timing how long it takes for an image of a cross drawn under the flask to disappear.

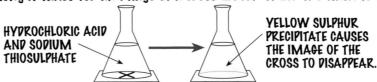

HYDROCHLORIC ACID AND SODIUM THIOSULPHATE

YELLOW SULPHUR PRECIPITATE CAUSES THE IMAGE OF THE CROSS TO DISAPPEAR.

We can change the rate of reaction by **HEATING THE SOLUTION**.
A small increase in temperature - about 10°C ...
... causes a large decrease in the time taken for the cross to disappear.
We can repeat this for different temperatures and plot a graph.
The reaction gets faster as the temperature increases.

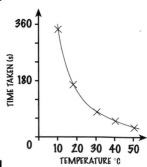

Other possible demonstrations are ...
• Measure the time it takes for marble chips to react completely and disappear in acid.
  A problem with this one is that not all marble chips are the same size!
• Use equal lengths of magnesium ribbon and time how long it takes for them to react completely and disappear in acid.

Surface Area Of Solid Reactants

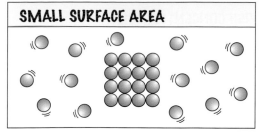

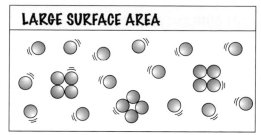

LARGE particles have a SMALL surface area in RELATION TO THEIR VOLUME - less particles are exposed and available for collisions. This means less collisions and a slower reaction.

SMALL particles have a LARGE surface area in RELATION TO THEIR VOLUME - more particles are exposed and available for collisions. This means more collisions and a faster reaction.

REACTION RATE IS SLOW

... where ～～ = SURFACE AREA

REACTION RATE IS FASTER

... where ～～ = SURFACE AREA

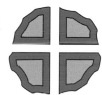

Demonstration

If we add hydrochloric acid to marble (calcium carbonate) ...

CALCIUM CARBONATE + HYDROCHLORIC ACID ⟶ CALCIUM CHLORIDE + WATER + CARBON DIOXIDE

$$CaCO_{3(s)} + 2HCl_{(aq)} \longrightarrow CaCl_{2(aq)} + H_2O_{(l)} + CO_{2(g)}$$

We can measure the rate of this reaction by measuring the amount of carbon dioxide given off every minute. The rate of reaction can be changed by first using marble chips and then an equal mass of finely crushed marble.

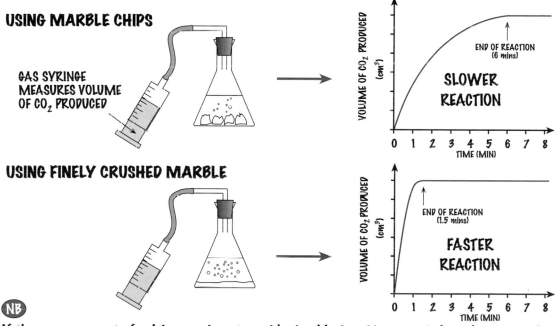

USING MARBLE CHIPS

GAS SYRINGE MEASURES VOLUME OF CO_2 PRODUCED

END OF REACTION (6 mins)
SLOWER REACTION

USING FINELY CRUSHED MARBLE

END OF REACTION (1.5 mins)
FASTER REACTION

(NB)

If the same amount of calcium carbonate and hydrochloric acid are used then the same volume of carbon dioxide is given off in total. It just takes different amounts of time.

Other possible demonstrations are ...

• Measure the time it takes for equal masses of different sized pieces of magnesium to react completely and disappear in the same volume of the same concentration of hydrochloric acid.

• Using a top pan balance, measure loss of mass against time for the reaction between marble and hydrochloric acid.

Concentration Of The Reactants

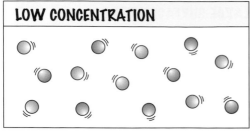

LOW CONCENTRATION	HIGH CONCENTRATION

MORE PARTICLES ...
... MORE COLLISIONS.

In a reaction where one or both reactants are in LOW concentrations the particles are spread out and will collide with each other less often resulting in fewer successful collisions.

In a reaction where one or both reactants are in HIGH concentrations the particles are crowded close together and will collide with each other more often, resulting in an increased number of successful collisions.

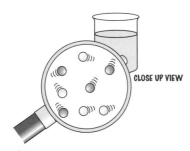

CLOSE UP VIEW

REACTION RATE IS SLOW

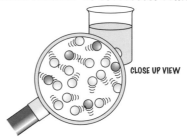

CLOSE UP VIEW

REACTION RATE IS FASTER

Demonstration

If we add hydrochloric acid to magnesium ribbon ...

MAGNESIUM + HYDROCHLORIC ACID $\longrightarrow$ MAGNESIUM + HYDROGEN CHLORIDE

$$Mg_{(s)} + 2HCl_{(aq)} \longrightarrow MgCl_{2(aq)} + H_{2(g)}$$

We can measure the rate of this reaction by measuring how long it takes for the magnesium to react completely and disappear in the acid.

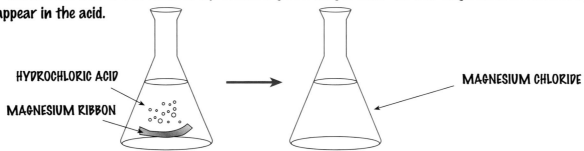

HYDROCHLORIC ACID

MAGNESIUM RIBBON

MAGNESIUM CHLORIDE

We can change the rate of reaction ...
... by CHANGING THE CONCENTRATION OF THE ACID.
An increase in concentration ...
... causes a decrease in the time taken ...
... for the reaction to end.
We can repeat for different concentrations ...
... and plot a graph.
The reaction gets faster as the concentration increases.

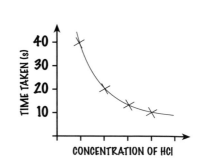

Other possible demonstrations are ...

• Using sodium thiosulphate and hydrochloric acid. Change the concentration of the sodium thiosulphate solution and time how long it takes for an image of a cross drawn under the flask to disappear due to sulphur being precipitated.

• Using marble chips and acid, measure how long it takes to collect a certain volume of carbon dioxide.

Using A Catalyst

A CATALYST is a substance which INCREASES the RATE of a chemical reaction, without being used up in the process. Catalysts are specific ie. different reactions need different catalysts. Because catalysts are not used up, only small amounts of catalysts are needed. Catalysts work by reducing the ACTIVATION ENERGY - the minimum energy needed for a reaction to happen.

Since catalysts lower the amount of energy needed for successful collisions, more collisions will be successful and the reaction will be faster. Also they provide a surface for the molecules to attach to, thereby increasing their chances of bumping into each other.

Demonstration

If we consider the decomposition of hydrogen peroxide ...

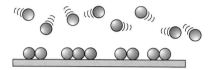

$$\text{HYDROGEN PEROXIDE} \longrightarrow \text{WATER} + \text{OXYGEN}$$
$$2H_2O_{2(aq)} \longrightarrow 2H_2O_{(l)} + O_{2(g)}$$

We can measure the rate of this reaction by measuring the amount of oxygen given off at one minute intervals. This reaction happens very slowly unless we add a catalyst of MANGANESE (IV) OXIDE. With a catalyst, plenty of fizzing can be seen as the oxygen is given off.

WITHOUT A CATALYST ...

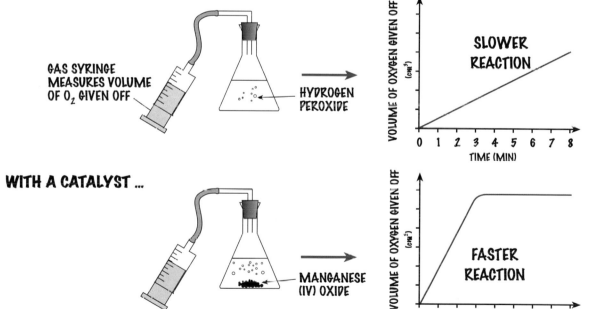

WITH A CATALYST ...

NB

If the same amount of hydrogen peroxide is used in both demonstrations then the same volume of oxygen is given off in total. It just takes different amounts of time.

Catalysts are used a lot in industrial processes to speed up reactions and make production more economical ...
... eg.   • the cracking of hydrocarbons using BROKEN POTTERY.
         • the manufacture of ammonia using IRON.

An ENZYME is a biological catalyst. Enzymes control the RATE OF CHEMICAL REACTIONS which occur in living organisms. The reactions take place in cells. Enzymes work best under certain conditions of TEMPERATURE and pH ...

Enzyme Activity And Temperature

The graph shows the effect of temperature ...
... on enzyme activity.

As the temperature rises, ...
... increased collisions between reactants and enzymes ...
... increase the enzyme activity ...
... up to the optimum temperature.
After this, an increase in temperature ...
... continues to cause increased collisions ...
... but the enzyme molecules ...
... become DENATURED (ie. permanently damaged) by the heat ...
... resulting in decreased enzyme activity ...
... or none at all.

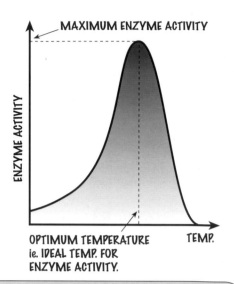

MAXIMUM ENZYME ACTIVITY

ENZYME ACTIVITY

OPTIMUM TEMPERATURE
ie. IDEAL TEMP. FOR
ENZYME ACTIVITY.   TEMP.

Different enzymes have different optimum temperatures. The ones in your body work best at about 37°C.

Enzyme Activity And pH

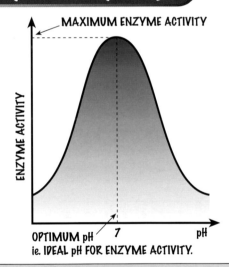

MAXIMUM ENZYME ACTIVITY

ENZYME ACTIVITY

OPTIMUM pH   7   pH
ie. IDEAL pH FOR ENZYME ACTIVITY.

The graph shows how changes in pH ...
... affect enzyme activity.

Notice that there is an optimum pH ...
... at which the enzyme works best.
As the pH increases or decreases ...
... about this point ...
... the enzyme becomes less effective.
Other enzymes may have a different
shaped graph eg. gastric protease.

The optimum pH of different enzymes can vary considerably ...
- ... the enzyme, amylase, in human saliva, works best at a pH of about 7.3.
- ... the enzyme, protease, which is in our stomach, needs to be in VERY acidic conditions to work well.

Why Enzymes Become Denatured

Enzymes are protein molecules with high specificity whose molecules have been assembled into particular shapes allowing the following to take place ...

ENZYME REACTANT → →

Reactant fits into active site   Reactant is broken down and enzyme can be re-used

..er, if a protein molecule is DENATURED ...
..4 TEMPERATURE or EXTREME pH ...
.. is changed irreversibly and the reactant no longer fits snugly ..
.. be broken down.

THE ATOM

ATOMIC STRUCTURE

NEUTRON

PROTON

ELECTRON

ATOMIC PARTICLE	RELATIVE MASS	RELATIVE CHARGE
PROTON	1	+1
NEUTRON	1	0
ELECTRON	0 (nearly!)	-1

The electrons are arranged in shells ...

HYDROGEN   BORON   SODIUM

ATOMIC NUMBER

This is denoted alongside the symbol for the element, and tells us how many protons it contains ...

$_3$Li $_7$N $_{26}$Fe

THE PERIODIC TABLE

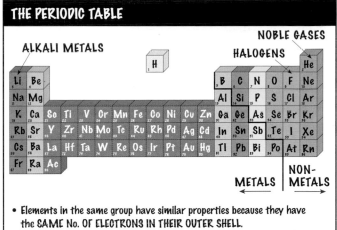

ALKALI METALS   NOBLE GASES   HALOGENS

METALS   NON-METALS

- Elements in the same group have similar properties because they have the SAME No. OF ELECTRONS IN THEIR OUTER SHELL.
- Elements of GROUP 1 become MORE REACTIVE as we move down the group because their outermost electron is more easily lost.
- Elements of GROUP 7 become LESS REACTIVE as we move down the group because an extra electron is less easily gained.
- Elements in GROUP 8 are UNREACTIVE because they have full outermost electron shells.

ELECTRON CONFIGURATION

The first shell can hold a maximum of 2 electrons, with each subsequent shell holding a maximum of 8.

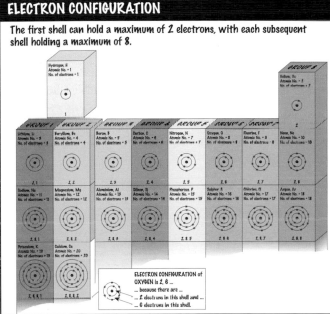

ELECTRON CONFIGURATION of OXYGEN is 2, 6 ...
... because there are ...
... 2 electrons in this shell and ...
... 6 electrons in this shell.

THE PROPERTIES OF HALOGENS

GROUP 7 - THE HALOGENS
- They ALL VARY IN COLOUR, ...
- ... and their BOILING POINT INCREASES as we go down the group.

HALOGEN	FLUORINE	CHLORINE	BROMINE	IODINE
BOILING POINT (°C)	-188°C	-34°C	59°C (melting pt -7°C)	184°C (melting pt 114°C)
COLOUR & PHYSICAL STATE AT ROOM TEMP.	PALE YELLOW VAPOUR	PALE GREEN VAPOUR	RED-BROWN LIQUID	GREY SOLID

REACTIONS OF CHLORINE WITH SODIUM AND IRON

SODIUM + CHLORINE ⟶ SODIUM CHLORIDE

$2Na_{(s)} + Cl_{2(g)} \longrightarrow 2NaCl_{(s)}$

IRON + CHLORINE ⟶ IRON (III) CHLORIDE

$2Fe_{(s)} + 3Cl_{2(g)} \longrightarrow 2FeCl_{3(s)}$

DISPLACEMENT REACTIONS OF THE HALOGENS

The halogens' atomic numbers increase as we go down the group and they become less reactive. This can be shown by the displacement reactions of the halogens with solutions of other halides.

	Potassium Chloride $KCl_{(aq)}$	Potassium Bromide $KBr_{(aq)}$	Potassium Iodide $KI_{(aq)}$
Chlorine Cl_2	✕	+ KCl + Bromine	+ KCl + Iodine
Bromine Br_2	No Reaction	✕	+ KBr + Iodine
Iodine I_2	No Reaction	No Reaction	✕

USES OF THE HALOGENS
- IODINE solution is used as an antiseptic.
- CHLORINE is used in WATER PURIFICATION eg. swimming pools and domestic water supplies, as it kills bacteria. It is also used for BLEACHING paper, wood and cloth.

EFFECT OF TEMPERATURE, SURFACE AREA AND CONCENTRATION

TEMPERATURE
- Higher temperature results in increased rate of reaction.
- Can be investigated using reaction between hydrochloric acid and sodium thiosulphate.

'COOL'   'HOT'

SLOW   FAST

SURFACE AREA
- Greater area results in increased rate of reaction.
- Can be investigated using the reactions between hydrochloric acid and large and small limestone chips.
- Large particles = small surface area.
- Small particles = large surface area.

'BIG PIECES'   'TINY PIECES'

SLOW   FAST

CONCENTRATION
- Greater concentration results in increased rate of reaction.
- Can be investigated using reaction between hydrochloric acid and magnesium.
- These 3 factors affect the NUMBER OF SUCCESSFUL COLLISIONS.

'DILUTE'   'CONCENTRATED'

SLOW   FAST

EFFECT OF CATALYSTS/ENZYMES

CATALYSTS
- Lower the energy needed for a successful collision. (The 'Activation Energy')
- Speed up a reaction without being used up.
- Can be investigated using decomposition of hydrogen peroxide with Manganese (IV) Oxide catalyst.

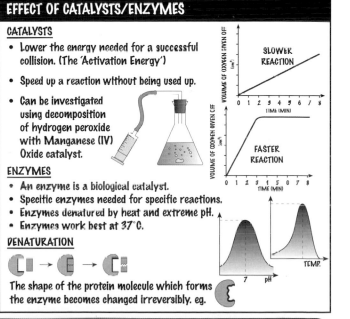

SLOWER REACTION

FASTER REACTION

ENZYMES
- An enzyme is a biological catalyst.
- Specific enzymes needed for specific reactions.
- Enzymes denatured by heat and extreme pH.
- Enzymes work best at 37°C.

DENATURATION

The shape of the protein molecule which forms the enzyme becomes changed irreversibly. eg.

Formation Of Crude Oil

- Crude oil was formed from the organic material ...
  ... of sea creatures that died millions of years ago.
- As they collected on the sea floor ...
  ... they were buried under layers of sedimentary rock which formed on top.
- In the absence of oxygen these sea creatures did not decay and ...
  ... due to the action of TEMPERATURE and PRESSURE they were changed into crude oil.

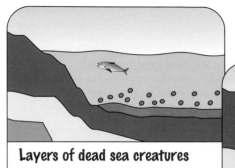

Layers of dead sea creatures formed on the sea bed.

Layers of sedimentary rock formed on top and the creatures became trapped.

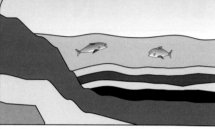

After millions of years oil began to form, in the absence of oxygen.

- Natural gas is usually formed with crude oil.

What Crude Oil Is

- Crude oil is a mixture of compounds most of which ...
- ... are MOLECULES made up of CARBON and HYDROGEN atoms only, called HYDROCARBONS.

The chemical structures of 4 simple hydrocarbons are shown below ...

METHANE, CH_4

A molecule made up of ...
... 1 carbon atom and 4 hydrogen atoms.

ETHANE, C_2H_6

A molecule made up of ...
... 2 carbon atoms and 6 hydrogen atoms.

PROPANE, C_3H_8

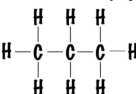

A molecule made up of ...
... 3 carbon atoms and 8 hydrogen atoms.

BUTANE, C_4H_{10}

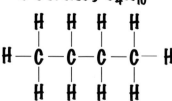

A molecule made up of ...
... 4 carbon atoms and 10 hydrogen atoms.

Fractional Distillation Of Crude Oil

Crude oil on its own isn't a great deal of use. However, since crude oil is a mixture of hydrocarbons which aren't chemically combined together, the properties of the hydrocarbons in crude oil remain unchanged and specific. This makes it possible to separate the hydrocarbons into their individual parts, or FRACTIONS, by FRACTIONAL DISTILLATION.

- EVAPORATE the oil by heating and then allow it to CONDENSE ...
  - ... at a RANGE OF DIFFERENT TEMPERATURES where it forms FRACTIONS.
    - Each of these fractions contain hydrocarbon molecules ...
      - ... with a SIMILAR NUMBER OF CARBON ATOMS.
        - This is done in a FRACTIONATING COLUMN.

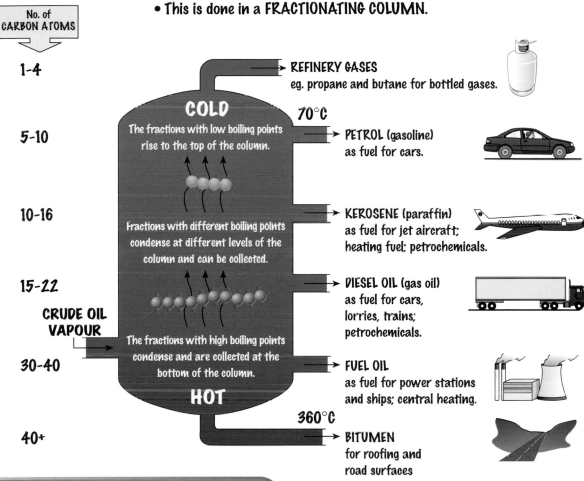

No. of CARBON ATOMS

1-4	REFINERY GASES eg. propane and butane for bottled gases.
5-10	PETROL (gasoline) as fuel for cars.
10-16	KEROSENE (paraffin) as fuel for jet aircraft; heating fuel; petrochemicals.
15-22	DIESEL OIL (gas oil) as fuel for cars, lorries, trains; petrochemicals.
30-40	FUEL OIL as fuel for power stations and ships; central heating.
40+	BITUMEN for roofing and road surfaces

COLD · 70°C

The fractions with low boiling points rise to the top of the column.

Fractions with different boiling points condense at different levels of the column and can be collected.

CRUDE OIL VAPOUR

The fractions with high boiling points condense and are collected at the bottom of the column.

HOT · 360°C

Properties Of The Different Fractions

The hydrocarbon molecules in each fraction vary in size. This affects their properties.

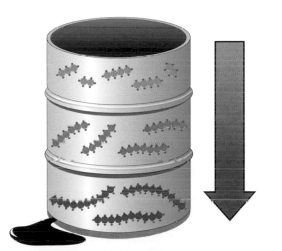

The LARGER the HYDROCARBON
ie. the greater the number of carbon atoms in a molecule:

1 The LESS EASILY IT FLOWS ...
... ie. the more viscous it is.

2 The LESS EASILY IT IGNITES ...
... ie. the less flammable it is.

3 The LESS VOLATILE IT IS ...
... ie. it doesn't vaporise as easily.

4 The HIGHER ITS BOILING POINT.
(see the fractionating column above).

A FUEL is a substance that releases useful amounts of ENERGY, when burned.
- Many fuels are HYDROCARBONS: compounds containing carbon and hydrogen.
- When a fuel burns it reacts with oxygen from the air.
- This addition of oxygen to a substance is known as OXIDATION.

Complete Combustion

When a HYDROCARBON burns and there is plenty of oxygen available ...
... COMPLETE COMBUSTION occurs, producing CARBON DIOXIDE and WATER ...
... and releasing ENERGY.
The apparatus below can be used to show this.

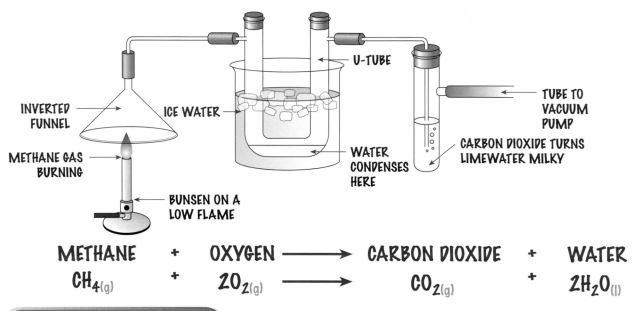

INVERTED FUNNEL

ICE WATER

U-TUBE

TUBE TO VACUUM PUMP

METHANE GAS BURNING

WATER CONDENSES HERE

CARBON DIOXIDE TURNS LIMEWATER MILKY

BUNSEN ON A LOW FLAME

$$METHANE + OXYGEN \longrightarrow CARBON\ DIOXIDE + WATER$$
$$CH_{4(g)} + 2O_{2(g)} \longrightarrow CO_{2(g)} + 2H_2O_{(l)}$$

Incomplete Combustion

Sometimes the fuel burns without sufficient oxygen eg. in a room with poor ventilation. Then INCOMPLETE COMBUSTION takes place and instead of carbon dioxide being produced, CARBON MONOXIDE is formed ...

$$METHANE + OXYGEN \longrightarrow CARBON\ MONOXIDE + WATER$$
$$2CH_{4(g)} + 3O_{2(g)} \longrightarrow 2CO_{(g)} + 4H_2O_{(l)}$$

If there is very little oxygen available, CARBON is produced ...

$$METHANE + OXYGEN \longrightarrow CARBON + WATER$$
$$CH_{4(g)} + O_{2(g)} \longrightarrow C_{(s)} + 2H_2O_{(l)}$$

Pollutant Gases

Although hydrocarbons do produce useful amounts of energy when they burn, the GASES they produce are POLLUTANTS.
- CARBON DIOXIDE contributes to the GREENHOUSE EFFECT.
- CARBON MONOXIDE, a toxic, colourless and odourless gas combines irreversibly with the haemoglobin in red blood cells reducing the oxygen-carrying capacity of the blood. This would result in death through a lack of oxygen reaching body tissues.

Incomplete combustion to produce carbon monoxide can occur in faulty gas appliances and other heating appliances.
Carbon monoxide detectors are now becoming an essential item in many homes. Better to be safe than sorry!

Sooty, yellow flame contains carbon which collects on the outside of a test tube containing water.

Alkanes – Saturated Hydrocarbons

The 'SPINE' of a HYDROCARBON is made up of a chain of CARBON ATOMS.
When these are joined by single covalent carbon—carbon bonds ...
... we say the HYDROCARBON is SATURATED and it is known as an ALKANE.

Hydrogen atoms can make ...
... 1 BOND EACH

Carbon atoms can make ...
... 4 BONDS EACH

The simplest alkane, METHANE, is made up of ...
... 4 HYDROGEN ATOMS and 1 CARBON ATOM.

$$CH_4$$

The next three simplest alkanes are ETHANE, PROPANE and BUTANE (see P42 for their structures). Because all their bonds are 'occupied' they are fairly UNREACTIVE, although they do burn well.

Alkenes – Unsaturated Hydrocarbons

The ALKENES are another kind of HYDROCARBON.
They are very similar to the alkanes ...
... except that two of the carbon atoms are joined by a DOUBLE COVALENT BOND.
The alkenes are known as UNSATURATED HYDROCARBONS ...
... because of the presence of the double covalent bond.
The simplest alkene is ETHENE, C_2H_4, which ...

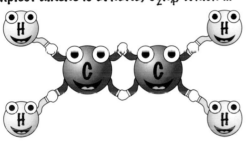

... is made up of 4 HYDROGEN ATOMS ...
... and 2 CARBON ATOMS.
As you can see ethene contains ...
... ONE DOUBLE CARBON—CARBON COVALENT BOND.

The next simplest alkene is PROPENE. The structures of ethene and propene are shown below.

ETHENE, C_2H_4

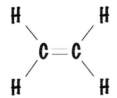

PROPENE, C_3H_6

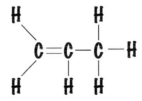

Test For An Alkene

A simple test to distinguish between alkenes and alkanes ...
... is that ALKENES will DECOLOURISE BROMINE WATER as the ALKENE REACTS WITH IT.
ALKANES have NO effect on bromine water!

e.g.   Ethene   +   Bromine Water   ⟶   COLOURLESS
       (colourless)   (yellow-brown)   SOLUTION

Supply And Demand For Crude Oil Fractions

The bar chart below shows the demand for the fractions of crude oil and the relative amounts of each fraction in crude oil.

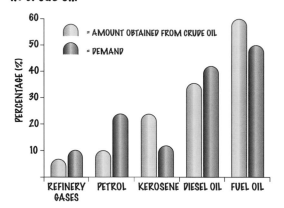

As you will see the demand for certain fractions exceeds the supply, especially the shorter chain hydrocarbons such as refinery gases and petrol. This is because they release energy more quickly by BURNING and there is a greater demand for them as fuels.

In order to increase the relative amounts of these fractions LONGER CHAIN HYDROCARBONS are broken down into SHORTER CHAIN HYDROCARBONS some of which have carbon—carbon double bonds.

This is known as CRACKING.

Cracking

A long chain hydrocarbon is heated until it vaporises; the vapour is then passed over a heated catalyst where a THERMAL DECOMPOSITION reaction takes place (see also P52).

In the laboratory, CRACKING can be carried out using the following apparatus ...

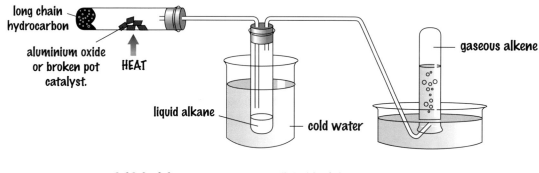

eg.

| DECANE | $\longrightarrow$ | OCTANE | + | ETHENE |
| $C_{10}H_{22}$ | $\longrightarrow$ | C_8H_{18} | + | C_2H_4 |

Industrial Cracking

Industrial cracking of long chain hydrocarbons ...
... is carried out at oil refineries ...
... using a 'CAT CRACKER'.
The long chain hydrocarbon ...

- ... is either mixed with a CATALYST of SILICON (IV) OXIDE ...
  ... and ALUMINIUM OXIDE ...
  ... and passed into a cat cracker at 500°C ...
  ... for a few seconds.

- ... or it is mixed with STEAM ...
  ... and passed into a cat cracker at 750°C ...
  ... for 0.1s to 0.5s.

Monomers To Polymers

One of the important uses of the alkenes which are produced during cracking, is the production of POLYMERS;... ... these are LONG CHAIN MOLECULES, some of which make up PLASTICS.

Because ALKENES are UNSATURATED, they are very good at joining together and when they do so without producing another substance, we call this ADDITION POLYMERISATION.

eg. the formation of poly(ethene) from ethene.

1 The small alkene molecules are called MONOMERS.

2 Their double bonds are easily broken.

3 ... large numbers of molecules can therefore be joined in this way.

> The resulting long chain molecule is a POLYMER - in this case POLY(ETHENE) ... often called POLYTHENE

A more convenient form of representing addition polymerisation is ...

$$\underset{H}{\overset{H}{C}}=\underset{H}{\overset{H}{C}} \;+\; \underset{H}{\overset{H}{C}}=\underset{H}{\overset{H}{C}} \;+\; \underset{H}{\overset{H}{C}}=\underset{H}{\overset{H}{C}} \;+\; \text{thousands more} \;\longrightarrow\; \cdots -\underset{H}{\overset{H}{C}}-\underset{H}{\overset{H}{C}}-\underset{H}{\overset{H}{C}}-\underset{H}{\overset{H}{C}}-\underset{H}{\overset{H}{C}}- \cdots \text{ and on and on ...}$$

ethene monomers (unsaturated)   poly(ethene) polymer (saturated)

Here is the general formula for addition polymerisation which can be used to represent the formation of a simple addition polymer.

$$n\left[\overset{|}{\underset{|}{C}}=\overset{|}{\underset{|}{C}} \right] \longrightarrow \left[\overset{|}{\underset{|}{C}}-\overset{|}{\underset{|}{C}} \right]_n$$

... where 'n' is a very large number.

For example, if we take ...

$$n\left[\underset{H}{\overset{H}{C}}=\underset{H}{\overset{H}{C}} \right] \longrightarrow \left[\underset{H}{\overset{H}{C}} \quad \underset{H}{\overset{H}{C}} \right]_n$$

... 'n' molecules of ethene to produce poly(ethene)..

... or, if we take ...

$$n\left[\underset{H}{\overset{H}{C}}=\underset{H}{\overset{CH_3}{C}} \right] \longrightarrow \left[\underset{H}{\overset{H}{C}} \quad \underset{H}{\overset{CH_3}{C}} \right]_n$$

... 'n' molecules of propene to produce poly(propene).

Uses Of Addition Polymers

POLY(ETHENE) ...

... film for packaging

... carrier bags

... moulded containers

... buckets

POLY(PROPENE) ...

... car bumpers and battery cases

... plastic chairs

... ropes

... fishing nets

... carpets

POLY(STYRENE) ...

... plastic models

... packaging

... insulation when expanded

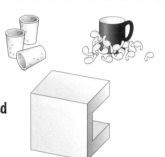

POLY(CHLOROETHENE), (polyvinyl chloride, PVC) ...

... pipes

... gutters

... window frames

... electrical insulation for cables

... floor tiles

... wall paper

Disposal Of Plastics

As we have seen, different plastics have many different uses. As it is such a convenient material this means that we produce a large amount of plastic waste. There are various ways of disposing of plastics, unfortunately some of them have consequent effects on the environment.

① **Use of landfill sites**

The problem with most plastics is that they are non-biodegradable. Microorganisms have no effect on them; they will not decompose and rot away. The use of landfill sites simply means that plastic waste builds up. However research is being carried out on the development of biodegradable plastics.

② **Burning**

Burning plastics produces air pollution. The production of carbon dioxide contributes to the greenhouse effect which results in global warming. Some plastics cannot be burned at all as they produce toxic fumes eg. the burning of PVC produces hydrogen chloride gas.

③ **Recycling**

This is an option which may well be worth persevering with. Unfortunately, there are many different types of plastic which all look the same! This means that sorting them into groups to be recycled can be a difficult and time-consuming process.

Enzymes are **BIOLOGICAL CATALYSTS** contained within **LIVING CELLS**. They are **PROTEIN MOLECULES** and every reaction in our body is catalysed by them.

They are also used in washing powders and in food and drink manufacture ...

1. Biological Washing Powders

Biological washing powders contain enzymes ...

... which break down tough stains on clothes ...

... such as food, blood, grass etc.

These washing powders work best ...

... at a specific temperature. Above this the enzymes are quickly destroyed.

2. Beer, Wine and Bread Making – Fermentation

Under the right temperature conditions enzymes in **YEAST** convert **SUGAR** into **ETHANOL** (alcohol) and **CARBON DIOXIDE**. This is **FERMENTATION** and it can easily be demonstrated ...

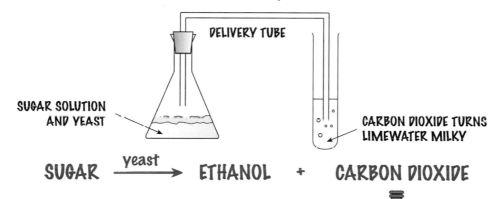

DELIVERY TUBE

SUGAR SOLUTION AND YEAST

CARBON DIOXIDE TURNS LIMEWATER MILKY

$$SUGAR \xrightarrow{\text{yeast}} ETHANOL + CARBON\ DIOXIDE$$

The **ETHANOL** produced during fermentation is used ...

... as the basis for the **BREWING** and **WINE-MAKING INDUSTRIES**.

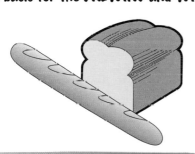

The **CARBON DIOXIDE** is used in **BAKING** ...

... to make the bread rise.

3. Yogurt and Cheese Making

Enzymes in microorganisms produce yoghurt from milk ...

... by converting lactose, ...

... a sugar found in milk, to **LACTIC ACID** ...

... so giving it a slightly sour taste.

In cheese making, ...

... **RENNET** (which contains enzymes) is added ...

... causing clotting which forms solid **CURDS** and liquid **WHEY**.

The curds are separated from the whey, ...

... pressed, and allowed to mature to produce cheese.

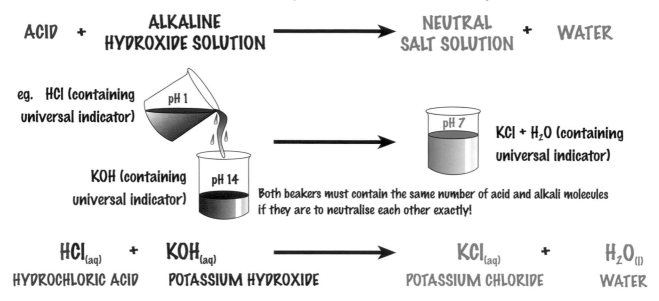

Neutralisation

Because acids and alkalis are 'chemical opposites' they can cancel each other out if they are added together in the correct amounts. This neutralisation reaction produces a neutral salt solution plus water.

ACID + ALKALINE HYDROXIDE SOLUTION $\longrightarrow$ NEUTRAL SALT SOLUTION + WATER

eg. HCl (containing universal indicator)

pH 1

KOH (containing universal indicator)   pH 14

Both beakers must contain the same number of acid and alkali molecules if they are to neutralise each other exactly!

pH 7   KCl + H_2O (containing universal indicator)

$HCl_{(aq)}$ + $KOH_{(aq)}$ $\longrightarrow$ $KCl_{(aq)}$ + $H_2O_{(l)}$

HYDROCHLORIC ACID   POTASSIUM HYDROXIDE   POTASSIUM CHLORIDE   WATER

The particular salt produced depends on the <u>METAL IN THE ALKALI</u>, and the <u>ACID USED</u>.

eg.   <u>SODIUM</u> HYDROXIDE + HYDRO<u>CHLORIC</u> ACID $\longrightarrow$ <u>SODIUM CHLORIDE</u> + WATER

OTHER EXAMPLES	HYDROCHLORIC ACID	SULPHURIC ACID	NITRIC ACID
+ SODIUM HYDROXIDE	$\longrightarrow$ SODIUM CHLORIDE + WATER	$\longrightarrow$ SODIUM SULPHATE + WATER	$\longrightarrow$ SODIUM NITRATE + WATER
+ POTASSIUM HYDROXIDE	$\longrightarrow$ POTASSIUM CHLORIDE + WATER	$\longrightarrow$ POTASSIUM SULPHATE + WATER	$\longrightarrow$ POTASSIUM NITRATE + WATER
+ CALCIUM HYDROXIDE	$\longrightarrow$ CALCIUM CHLORIDE + WATER	$\longrightarrow$ CALCIUM SULPHATE + WATER	$\longrightarrow$ CALCIUM NITRATE + WATER

Production Of Fertilisers

Some salts made by neutralisation reactions can be used as fertilisers. However, since a key ingredient of fertilisers is nitrogen, ammonia solution is often reacted with an acid to form an ammonium salt ...

AMMONIA + SULPHURIC ACID $\longrightarrow$ AMMONIUM SULPHATE

$2NH_{3(aq)}$ + $H_2SO_{4(aq)}$ $\longrightarrow$ $(NH_4)_2SO_{4(aq)}$

As you can see, each molecule of ammonium sulphate contains 2 atoms of nitrogen. An equally good fertiliser can be made by using nitric acid instead of sulphuric acid ...

AMMONIA + NITRIC ACID $\longrightarrow$ AMMONIUM NITRATE

$NH_{3(aq)}$ + $HNO_{3(aq)}$ $\longrightarrow$ $NH_4NO_{3(aq)}$

Once again, the salt produced contains 2 atoms of nitrogen per molecule of salt, and as a result is an excellent fertiliser.

NITRATE OF AMMONIA

Limestone is a SEDIMENTARY ROCK ...
... which consists mainly of CALCIUM CARBONATE.
It is cheap ...
    ... easy to obtain ...
        ... and has many uses.

1. Production Of Calcium Oxide And Calcium Hydroxide

Excess ACIDITY of soils can cause crop failure.
Alkalis can be 'washed out' by acid rain.
Powdered limestone can be used to neutralise acid soils ...
... but it works quite slowly.
However, it can be used to produce CALCIUM OXIDE (quicklime) ...
... and CALCIUM HYDROXIDE (slaked lime), ...
... both of which are used by farmers to neutralise acid soils.

- When CALCIUM CARBONATE is heated in a lime kiln, at a temperature of above 1000°C, a THERMAL DECOMPOSITION reaction takes place ...

$$\text{CALCIUM CARBONATE} \xrightarrow{\text{HEAT}} \text{CALCIUM OXIDE} + \text{CARBON DIOXIDE}$$
$$\text{(limestone)} \qquad\qquad \text{(quicklime)}$$

$$CaCO_{3(s)} \xrightarrow{\text{HEAT}} CaO_{(s)} + CO_{2(g)}$$

- This can then be 'SLAKED' with water to produce CALCIUM HYDROXIDE (SLAKED LIME).

$$\text{CALCIUM OXIDE} + \text{WATER} \longrightarrow \text{CALCIUM HYDROXIDE}$$
$$\text{(quicklime)} \qquad\qquad\qquad\qquad\qquad \text{(slaked lime)}$$

$$CaO_{(s)} + H_2O_{(l)} \longrightarrow Ca(OH)_{2(s)}$$

In effect, therefore, a farmer who chooses to neutralise his acid soil using calcium oxide is doing the same as a farmer who adds calcium hydroxide, since the oxide reacts with the water in the soil to produce calcium hydroxide.

2. Production Of Glass, Cement And Iron

GLASS

- Glass is made by mixing
... LIMESTONE, SAND and ...
... SODA (sodium carbonate) ...
... and heating the mixture ...
... until it melts.

- When cool, it is TRANSPARENT.

CEMENT

- Powdered LIMESTONE, ...
... powdered CLAY and ...
... a small amount of CALCIUM SULPHATE ...
... are roasted in a ROTARY KILN ...
... to produce dry cement.

CEMENT

IRON

- LIMESTONE reacts with impurities ...
... including sand in the BLAST FURNACE ...
... to form MOLTEN SLAG ...
... which floats on top of the molten iron.

- The molten slag is then tapped off.

IRON ORE, LIMESTONE AND COKE

WASTE GASES

HOT AIR

molten slag tapped here

HOT AIR

molten iron tapped here

Thermal Decomposition

This is when a substance BREAKS DOWN into simpler substances when heated. If we take COPPER CARBONATE and heat it ...

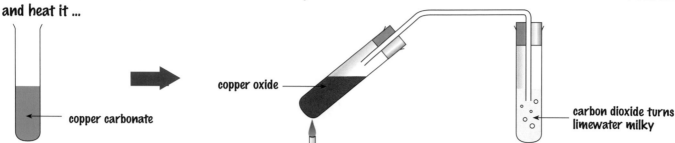

copper carbonate

copper oxide

carbon dioxide turns limewater milky

...we find that the BLUISH-GREEN COPPER CARBONATE decomposes into BLACK COPPER OXIDE and CARBON DIOXIDE which turns the limewater milky.

COPPER CARBONATE $\longrightarrow$ COPPER OXIDE + CARBON DIOXIDE

$CuCO_{3(s)} \longrightarrow CuO_{(s)} + CO_{2(g)}$

Other examples of thermal decomposition reactions are ...
- ... the CRACKING of LONG CHAIN HYDROCARBONS (see P46)
- ... the production of CALCIUM OXIDE from CALCIUM CARBONATE in a lime kiln (see P51 and below).

Limewater

LIMEWATER is an AQUEOUS SOLUTION OF CALCIUM HYDROXIDE. It is used to test for CARBON DIOXIDE as it turns from COLOURLESS to MILKY when the gas is bubbled through it. Limewater can be produced in the laboratory.

STAGE 1 Thermal decomposition of limestone.

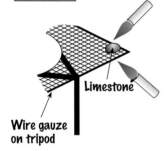

Limestone

Wire gauze on tripod

Place some limestone (calcium carbonate) on the edge of a gauze on a tripod and heat it strongly for a few minutes making sure that the limestone glows.

CALCIUM CARBONATE $\longrightarrow$ CALCIUM OXIDE + CARBON DIOXIDE

$CaCO_{3(s)} \longrightarrow CaO_{(s)} + CO_{2(s)}$

STAGE 2 Add water to the calcium oxide.

Let the calcium oxide cool down and use tongs to put it on a watch glass. Add water, drop by drop onto the calcium oxide until there is no more reaction.

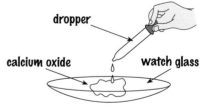

dropper

calcium oxide

watch glass

CALCIUM OXIDE + WATER $\longrightarrow$ CALCIUM HYDROXIDE

$CaO_{(s)} + H_2O_{(l)} \longrightarrow Ca(OH)_{2(aq)}$

STAGE 3 Filter the mixture into a test tube and divide into two portions, ...

...and bubble exhaled air through one portion ...   ... add universal indicator solution to the other portion ...

... it turns milky proving that the filtrate is limewater

... it turns PURPLE proving the existence of an ALKALI which limewater is.

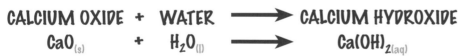

CALCIUM HYDROXIDE + CARBON DIOXIDE $\longrightarrow$ CALCIUM CARBONATE + WATER

$Ca(OH)_{2(aq)} + CO_{2(g)} \longrightarrow CaCO_{3(s)} + H_2O_{(l)}$

CRUDE OIL AND FRACTIONAL DISTILLATION

CRUDE OIL ... formed by HEAT and PRESSURE
in the ABSENCE of OXYGEN on ORGANIC MATERIAL trapped beneath layers
of sedimentary rocks for millions of years.

• Crude oil is a mixture of compounds most
  of which are made up of CARBON and HYDROGEN
  atoms only, called HYDROCARBONS.

The larger the hydrocarbon molecule ...
• ... the LESS EASILY IT FLOWS.
• ... the LESS EASILY IT IGNITES.

This mixture can be separated by DISTILLATION.

FRACTIONAL DISTILLATION ...
• The crude oil is heated and allowed
  to CONDENSE at a RANGE OF DIFFERENT
  TEMPERATURES.
• The 'fractions' formed contain
  HYDROCARBON molecules with a
  similar number of carbon atoms.
• This is done in a fractionating
  column shown opposite.

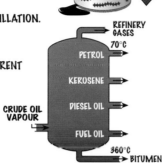

REFINERY GASES 70°C
PETROL
KEROSENE
DIESEL OIL
CRUDE OIL VAPOUR
FUEL OIL
360°C
BITUMEN

ALKANES AND ALKENES

ALKANES ... are 'saturated' hydrocarbons in which the carbon atoms
are joined together by SINGLE COVALENT BONDS.

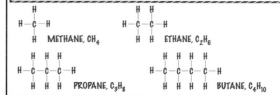

METHANE, CH_4 ETHANE, C_2H_6

PROPANE, C_3H_8 BUTANE, C_4H_{10}

ALKENES ... are 'unsaturated' hydrocarbons in which there is at least
one DOUBLE COVALENT BOND between the carbon atoms.

ETHENE C_2H_4 PROPENE C_3H_6

They are reactive because the double bond allows them to join
with other molecules to form POLYMERS. Alkenes are identified
by decolourising BROMINE WATER.

eg. Ethene (colourless) + Bromine Water (yellow-brown) → COLOURLESS SOLUTION

COMBUSTION AND CRACKING

Many fuels are HYDROCARBONS, which when burnt react with oxygen in
the air (oxidation).

COMPLETE COMBUSTION:

| METHANE | + | OXYGEN | → | CARBON DIOXIDE | + | WATER |
| $CH_{4(g)}$ | + | $2O_{2(g)}$ | | $CO_{2(g)}$ | + | $2H_2O_{(l)}$ |

INCOMPLETE COMBUSTION:

| METHANE | + | OXYGEN | → | CARBON MONOXIDE | + | WATER |
| $2CH_{4(g)}$ | + | $3O_{2(g)}$ | | $2CO_{(g)}$ | + | $4H_2O_{(l)}$ |

If there is even less oxygen ...

| METHANE | + | OXYGEN | → | CARBON | + | WATER |
| $CH_{4(g)}$ | + | $O_{2(g)}$ | | $C_{(s)}$ | + | $2H_2O_{(l)}$ |

• Carbon monoxide is a toxic gas and can be produced by faulty heating appliances.

CRACKING ...
• Shorter chain hydrocarbons are in greater demand because
  they release ENERGY QUICKLY.
• Long chain hydrocarbons are therefore 'CRACKED' into shorter chains by
  passing their vapour over a heated catalyst causing THERMAL DECOMPOSITION.
• Some of these shorter chain hydrocarbons have carbon - carbon double bonds
  ie. they are ALKENES

INDUSTRIAL CRACKING ... uses a catalyst of silicon (iv) oxide and Aluminium oxide
and a temp of 500°C. Or if steam is used (750°C) the time is reduced.

ADDITION POLYMERS

ADDITION POLYMERISATION ... is when alkene monomers join together to form
a polymer and no other substance eg. lots of ETHENE molecules join up to form
POLYETHENE.
The general formula is ...

$n \begin{pmatrix} C - C \end{pmatrix} \rightarrow \begin{pmatrix} C - C \end{pmatrix}_n$

So for ethene to poly(ethene) we would write ...

ethene → poly(ethene)

USES OF ADDITION POLYMERS

POLY(ETHENE) ...	POLY(STYRENE) ...	POLY(PROPENE) ...	POLY(CHLOROETHENE),
... film for packaging	... plastic models	... car bumpers and	(polyvinyl chloride, PVC) ...
... carrier bags	... packaging	battery cases	... pipes
... moulded containers	... insulation when	... plastic chairs	... gutters
... buckets	expanded	... ropes	... window frames
		... fishing nets	... electrical insulation
		... carpets	for cables
			... floor tiles
			... wall paper

DISPOSAL OF PLASTICS
LANDFILL SITES - Unfortunately most plastics are not biodegradable.
BURNING - Can produce toxic fumes as well as CO_2.
RECYCLING - Time consuming but becoming a necessity.

ENZYMES AND NEUTRALISATION

ENZYMES

❶ In Biological washing powders ... at a specific temperature the enzyme
  breaks down organic stains etc.
❷ In Beer, Wine and Bread making ... here, enzymes in yeast convert sugar
  into alcohol and carbon dioxide. The alcohol produced during fermentation
  is a critical part of the beer and wine. The CO_2 makes bread rise.
❸ In yoghurt and cheese making ... enzymes convert lactose to lactic acid,
  in yoghurt, and Rennet causes curd production in cheese making.

NEUTRALISATION ...

ACID + ALKALINE HYDROXIDE → NEUTRAL SALT + WATER
       SOLUTION   SOLUTION

eg. Hydrochloric + Potassium → Potassium + Water
    Acid   Hydroxide   Chloride

PREPARING SALTS ...
the salt produced in a reaction between an acid and an alkali depends on ...
.. • THE ACID USED .. • THE METAL IN THE ALKALI.
HYDROCHLORIC ACID + SODIUM HYDROXIDE → SODIUM CHLORIDE + WATER
In neutralisation reactions ...
  HYDROCHLORIC ACID produces CHLORIDE SALTS
  SULPHURIC ACID produces SULPHATE SALTS
  NITRIC ACID produces NITRATE SALTS
Using ammonia to neutralise sulphuric or nitric acid produces ammonium sulphate
or ammonium nitrate both of which are used as fertilisers due to their high proportion
of nitrogen.

LIMESTONE, THERMAL DECOMPOSITION AND LIMEWATER

LIMESTONE ... is made mainly of CALCIUM CARBONATE.
• It can be used as a NEUTRALISING AGENT either directly or
  as CALCIUM HYDROXIDE

*CALCIUM CARBONATE --HEAT--> CALCIUM OXIDE + CARBON DIOXIDE
  (limestone)   (quicklime)

CALCIUM OXIDE --WATER--> CALCIUM HYDROXIDE
  (quicklime)   (slaked lime)

• It is used in glass making LIMESTONE + SAND + SODA --HEAT--> GLASS
• It is used in cement making where it is heated in a kiln with powdered clay.

THERMAL DECOMPOSITION ... the reaction above * is an example of this, as
is the heating of copper carbonate.

COPPER CARBONATE → COPPER OXIDE + CARBON DIOXIDE
$CuCO_{3(s)}$ → $CuO_{(s)}$ + $CO_{2(g)}$

LIMEWATER

CALCIUM OXIDE + WATER → CALCIUM HYDROXIDE (Limewater)
$CaO_{(s)}$ + $H_2O_{(l)}$ → $Ca(OH)_{2(aq)}$

When CO_2 is bubbled through limewater it goes 'milky'.
$CaOH_{2(aq)}$ + $CO_{2(g)}$ → $CaCO_{3(s)}$ + $H_2O_{(l)}$

An **ELECTRICAL CURRENT** will flow through an **ELECTRICAL COMPONENT** (or device) ...
... if there is a **VOLTAGE** across the ends of the component.
CELLS and **BATTERIES** supply **DIRECT CURRENT** which means that the current ...
... always flows in the same direction.
In the following circuits each cell and lamp are identical ...

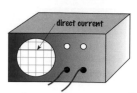

... a d.c. supply connected to an oscilloscope.

CIRCUIT 1

Cell provides voltage ...   A direct current flows and ...
... across the lamp.   ... the lamp lights up.

The amount of current that flows through the component above depends on two things ...

... 1. The Voltage Of The Source

As the voltage of a source increases, so the voltage across a component also increases, and ...
... a **HIGHER CURRENT** flows through the component.

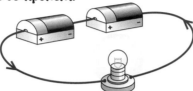

CIRCUIT 2

Two cells together provide ...   A bigger current now flows and ...
... a bigger voltage across the lamp.   ... the lamp lights up more brightly
                                            (compared to circuit 1).

... 2. The Resistance In A Circuit

COMPONENTS RESIST the **FLOW** of **CURRENT THROUGH THEM**. They have **RESISTANCE**.
The **GREATER** the **RESISTANCE** in a circuit ...
... the **SMALLER** the **CURRENT** that flows for a **PARTICULAR VOLTAGE**.

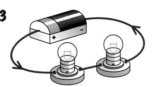

CIRCUIT 3

Two lamps together have a   A smaller current now flows and ...
GREATER RESISTANCE.   ... the lamps light up less brightly
                                            (compared to circuit 1).

Measurement Of Voltage And Current

The voltage across a component in a circuit is measured in volts (V) using a **VOLTMETER** connected in **PARALLEL**
across the component ...

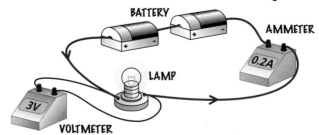

... while the current flowing through a component in a circuit is measured in amperes (A) using an **AMMETER**
connected in **SERIES**.

Standard Symbols For Drawing Circuit Diagrams

The following standard symbols are used in circuit diagrams.

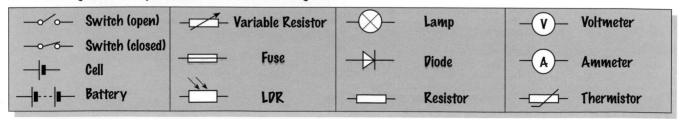

—∘/∘— Switch (open)	⟋ Variable Resistor	⊗ Lamp	Ⓥ Voltmeter
—∘⌒∘— Switch (closed)			
—┤├— Cell	▭ Fuse	▷| Diode	Ⓐ Ammeter
—┤├--┤├— Battery	⟋ LDR	▭ Resistor	⟋ Thermistor

Components Connected In Series

In a series circuit, ALL COMPONENTS are connected ONE AFTER THE OTHER in ONE LOOP, going from ONE TERMINAL of the BATTERY to the OTHER. When components are connected in series ...

1 The same CURRENT flows through each COMPONENT, ...
... regardless of the resistance of each component.

ie. $A_1 = A_2 = A_3$
eg. each ammeter reading is 0.1A.

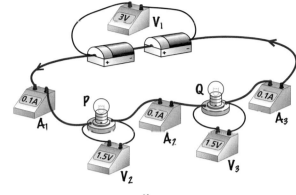

2 The VOLTAGE ...
... supplied by the battery is DIVIDED UP ...
... between the TWO COMPONENTS in the circuit.

ie. $V_1 = V_2 + V_3$

However ...
... in our circuit both bulbs have the same resistance ...
... and the voltage is divided equally ...
... but if one bulb had twice the resistance of the other, ...
... then the voltage would be divided differently ie. 2V and 1V.

Components Connected In Parallel

Components connected in parallel are connected SEPARATELY in their OWN LOOP going from ONE TERMINAL of the BATTERY to the OTHER. When components are connected in parallel ...

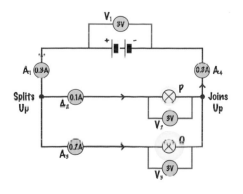

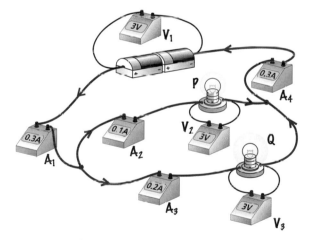

1 The TOTAL CURRENT in the main circuit ...
... is equal to the SUM of the CURRENTS ...
... through the separate components.

ie. $A_1 = A_2 + A_3 = A_4$

eg. 0.3A = 0.1A + 0.2A = 0.3A
In our circuit bulb P has twice the resistance of bulb Q ...
... and so only 0.1A passes through bulb P ...
... while 0.2A passes through bulb Q.
However ...
... if each bulb did have the same resistance ...
... then the current passing through each bulb ...
... would be the same.

2 The VOLTAGE ACROSS ...
... EACH COMPONENT is the SAME ...
... regardless of the resistance of the component.
(... and is equal to the voltage of the battery).

ie. $V_1 = V_2 = V_3$

eg. each bulb has a voltage of 3V across it.

V = I R

RESISTANCE is a measure of how hard it is to get a CURRENT through a component at a particular VOLTAGE. Voltage, current and resistance are related by the equation:

VOLTAGE (V) = CURRENT (A) x RESISTANCE (Ω)

(we use the letter I for current)

Examples

(1) Calculate the reading on the voltmeter in the circuit below if the bulb has a resistance of **15 ohms**.

Using our equation: VOLTAGE = CURRENT x RESISTANCE
= 0.2A x 15Ω
= 3V

(2) Calculate the reading on the ammeter in the circuit below if the bulb has a resistance of **20 ohms**.

Using our equation: CURRENT = $\dfrac{\text{VOLTAGE}}{\text{RESISTANCE}}$
(rearranged using our formula triangle.)

= $\dfrac{6.0\ V}{20\ \Omega}$

= 0.3A

Resistance Of A Light Dependent Resistor And A Thermistor

These are components whose resistance depends on the external conditions surrounding the components.

LIGHT DEPENDENT RESISTOR (LDR)

The resistance of an LDR ...
... depends on the amount of light falling on it.

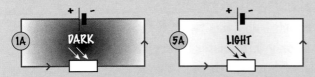

Its RESISTANCE DECREASES as the ...
... AMOUNT OF LIGHT FALLING ON IT INCREASES ...
... as shown by this graph.

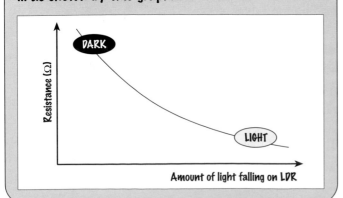

THERMISTOR

The resistance of a thermistor ...
... depends on its temperature.

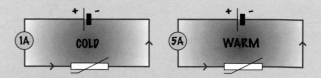

Its RESISTANCE DECREASES as the ...
... TEMPERATURE OF THE THERMISTOR INCREASES ...
... as shown by this graph.

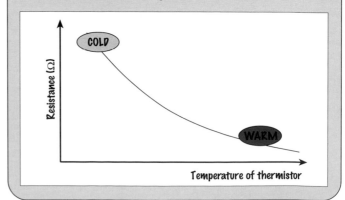

Using A Variable Resistor

A VARIABLE RESISTOR is a component whose resistance can be varied. If we wanted to investigate experimentally how current varies with voltage for a particular device then we would need to include a variable resistor in the circuit. A range of current and voltage readings for that device can then be obtained by simply moving the sliding contact of the variable resistor from one end to the other as shown below.

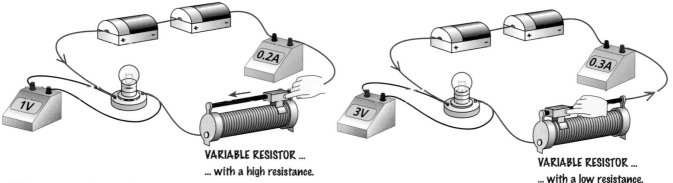

VARIABLE RESISTOR ...
... with a high resistance.

VARIABLE RESISTOR ...
... with a low resistance.

We can now investigate experimentally the following devices ...

1. Fixed Value Resistor

Providing the TEMPERATURE of the RESISTOR ...
... STAYS CONSTANT then ...
... EQUAL INCREASES IN VOLTAGE ACROSS THE RESISTOR ...
... PRODUCE EQUAL INCREASES IN CURRENT ...
... THROUGH THE RESISTOR.
ie. if one doubles, the other doubles etc ...
... regardless of which direction the current is flowing.

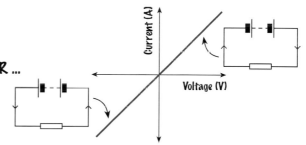

2. Filament Lamp

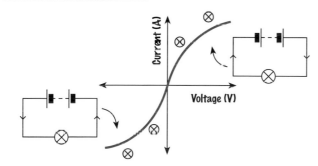

As the TEMPERATURE of the ...
... FILAMENT INCREASES and the ...
... bulb gets brighter then the ...
... RESISTANCE OF THE FILAMENT LAMP INCREASES, ...
... regardless of which direction the current is flowing.
Consequently, you don't get the same increase in current for a given increase in voltage.

3. Diode

A diode allows a CURRENT to flow through it ...
... in ONE DIRECTION ONLY;
when the voltage across it ...
... reaches a certain value.
It has a VERY HIGH RESISTANCE ...
... in the REVERSE DIRECTION ...
... and no current flows ...
... regardless of the voltage across it.

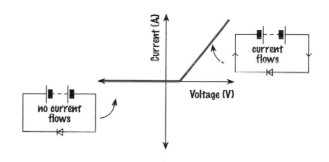

Alternating Current

This type of current changes its direction of flow ...
... back and forth continuously.
The MAINS ELECTRICITY SUPPLY is ALTERNATING CURRENT ...
... which is capable of providing dangerous currents ...
... that can cause serious injury or even death if not used safely.
Most electrical appliances are connected to the mains supply using a CABLE and a 3-PIN PLUG ...
... which is inserted into a SOCKET on the ring main circuit.

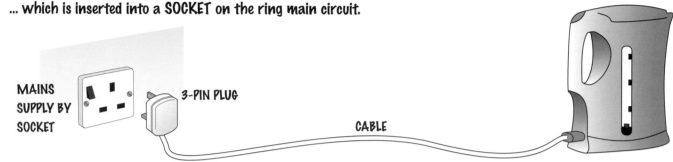

alternating current

... an a.c. supply connected to an oscilloscope.

MAINS SUPPLY BY SOCKET

3-PIN PLUG

CABLE

A typical appliance - a kettle

3-Pin Plug

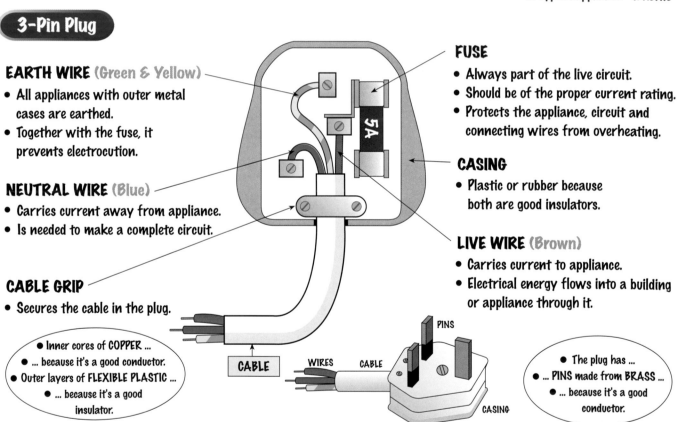

EARTH WIRE (Green & Yellow)
- All appliances with outer metal cases are earthed.
- Together with the fuse, it prevents electrocution.

NEUTRAL WIRE (Blue)
- Carries current away from appliance.
- Is needed to make a complete circuit.

CABLE GRIP
- Secures the cable in the plug.

- Inner cores of COPPER ...
- ... because it's a good conductor.
- Outer layers of FLEXIBLE PLASTIC ...
- ... because it's a good insulator.

FUSE
- Always part of the live circuit.
- Should be of the proper current rating.
- Protects the appliance, circuit and connecting wires from overheating.

CASING
- Plastic or rubber because both are good insulators.

LIVE WIRE (Brown)
- Carries current to appliance.
- Electrical energy flows into a building or appliance through it.

CABLE   WIRES   CABLE   PINS   CASING

- The plug has ...
- ... PINS made from BRASS ...
- ... because it's a good conductor.

It is very important that all plugs are wired correctly as above, with NO errors, for our own safety.
Below are five examples of dangerously wired plugs!

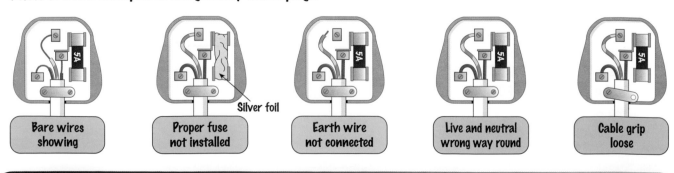

| Bare wires showing | Proper fuse not installed | Earth wire not connected | Live and neutral wrong way round | Cable grip loose |

Silver foil

Fuses

A FUSE is a SHORT, THIN piece of WIRE with a LOW MELTING POINT.
When the CURRENT passing through it EXCEEDS the CURRENT RATING of the fuse, ...
... the fuse wire gets HOT and MELTS or BREAKS.
This PREVENTS DAMAGE to the APPLIANCE, CIRCUIT and CONNECTING WIRES through the
possibility of OVERHEATING.

CURRENT LARGER THAN CURRENT RATING OF FUSE → FUSE BURNS OUT → CIRCUIT IS BROKEN → NO CURRENT FLOWS → APPLIANCE, CIRCUIT AND CONNECTING WIRES ARE PROTECTED

However, for this safety system to work properly the CURRENT RATING of the fuse must be
JUST ABOVE THE NORMAL CURRENT RATING of the appliance.

Example of a fuse in action

Normally the current flowing ...
... is BELOW the current rating ...
... of the fuse ...
... and the appliance (hairdrier) ...
... works properly.
However ...
... a fault occurs inside the appliance ...

... and the live wire makes contact ...
... with the neutral wire.
The current now flowing is ABOVE
... the current rating of the fuse ...
... because there is less resistance.
This causes the fuse wire to get ...
... hotter and hotter until ...

... it gets so hot ...
... it melts!
The circuit is now broken.
No current flows and ...
... there is no danger of ...
... further damage to the appliance ...
... or injury to the user.

Insulation And Double Insulation

All electrical appliances should have proper insulation where there is no possible contact with any 'bare wires'
or 'live metal parts' within the plug, between the plug and appliance, or within the appliance itself.
Some appliances are DOUBLE INSULATED where ...
... all METAL PARTS INSIDE the appliance are COMPLETELY INSULATED from ...
... any OUTSIDE PART of the appliance which may be handled.
These appliances DO NOT HAVE AN EARTH WIRE although they are still PROTECTED BY A FUSE.

— HIGHER TIER —

Residual Current Circuit Breaker (RCCB)

These devices detect any difference between the currents in the live and neutral conductors.
When this happens due to a leak of current to earth ...
... the circuit is immediately broken to protect the user.
They can be easily reset.
It is advisable to use an RCCB when using certain appliances ...
... such as a lawnmower or hedgecutter because the user is making good contact with earth.

Energy Transfer In Resistors

A RESISTOR is a component which has a FIXED RESISTANCE. When an electric current passes through a resistor there is an energy transfer as electrical energy is transferred into heat energy. This happens because moving electrons collide with atoms within the resistor giving up their energy, which results in the temperature of the resistor increasing.

This heating effect of an electric current is used in a variety of appliances ...

You should remember though that not all appliances are designed to transfer electrical energy into heat energy.

The Kilowatt-hour

When an energy transfer takes place in an electrical appliance, there is a price to pay. If one appliance transfers more electrical energy than another appliance then it will cost more to use that appliance for the same time period. Energy from the mains supply is measured in kilowatt-hours (kWh). An electrical appliance transfers 1kWh of energy if it transfers energy at the rate of 1 kilowatt (1000 watts) for 1 hour. For example ...

- A 100 watt light bulb   ... transfers 1 kWh of energy if it is switched on for 10 hours.

- A 200 watt television   ... transfers 1 kWh of energy if it is switched on for 5 hours.

- A 500 watt vacuum cleaner   ... transfers 1 kWh of energy if it is switched on for 2 hours.

- A 1000 watt toaster   ... transfers 1 kWh of energy if it is switched on for 1 hour.

- A 2000 watt kettle   ... transfers 1 kWh of energy if it is switched on for $^1/_2$ hour (30 mins).

Kilowatt-hour Calculations

In order to work out the cost of electricity we need to use the following equation ...

$$\text{COST} = \text{POWER (kW)} \times \text{TIME (h)} \times \text{COST OF 1kWh}$$

Examples

1 A 0.2 kW television is switched on for 10 hours. How much does it cost if electricity is 8 pence per kWh?

Using our equation: COST = POWER x TIME x COST OF 1kWh
                        = 0.2 kW x 10h x 8p
                        = 16 pence

2 A 2000 watt electric hot plate is switched on for 90 minutes. How much does it cost if electricity is 8 pence per kWh?

Using our equation: COST = POWER x TIME x COST OF 1kWh   *(POWER IN kW / TIME IN HOURS)*
                        = 2 kW x 1.5h x 8p
                        = 24 pence

And finally, to do these calculations, you must remember ...
         ... to make sure the POWER is in kilowatts, and ...
         ... to make sure that the TIME is in HOURS.

GENERATORS AND TRANSFORMERS

Energy and Electricity 8

Generators

If a **MAGNET** is rotated inside a **COIL OF WIRE** ...
... the **MAGNETIC FIELD** around the magnet is 'cut' by the wire causing ...
... an **ELECTRIC CURRENT** to be generated in the wire providing it is part of a complete circuit.
GENERATORS use this principle for generating electricity, for example ...

... on a small scale, as in a bicycle dynamo.

- Movement of the bicycle wheel causes a magnet ...
  ... to rotate inside a coil of wire.
- An electric current is generated in the wire ...
  ... as long as there is movement of the wheel.
- The faster the wheel moves ...
  ... the greater the electric current generated.

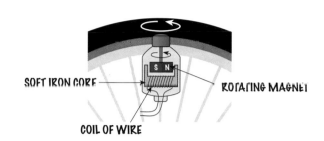

SOFT IRON CORE — ROTATING MAGNET
COIL OF WIRE

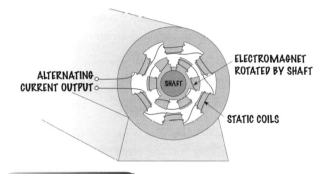

ALTERNATING CURRENT OUTPUT
ELECTROMAGNET ROTATED BY SHAFT
SHAFT
STATIC COILS

... on a large scale, as in a power station.

- Energy from a furnace or reactor ...
  ... is used to turn water into steam ...
  ... which drives the turbine shafts.
- These rotating shafts are connected ...
  ... to an electromagnet in the generator.
- As the electromagnet rotates ...
  ... an alternating current is generated in the static coils.

Transformers

Electricity generated at **POWER STATIONS** is distributed to homes, schools, shops, factories etc. all over the country by a network of cables called the **NATIONAL GRID**. **TRANSFORMERS** are used to change the voltage of an a.c. supply, and are used both before and after transmission through the grid.

- Before transmission onto the **GRID** ...
  - ... **TRANSFORMERS** are used to 'STEP-UP'...
    - ... the **VOLTAGE** of the electricity generated.
      - Doing this decreases the electric current flowing ...
        - ... which reduces the amount of energy lost during transmission.

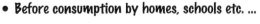

POWER STATION
STEP-UP TRANSFORMER
25,000V
400,000V
POWER LINES
STEP-DOWN TRANSFORMER
HOUSES, SHOPS etc.
400,000V
230V

- Before consumption by homes, schools etc. ...
  - ... **LOCAL TRANSFORMERS** are used to 'STEP-DOWN' ...
    - ... the voltage to a level which is safe to use.
      - Doing this increases the electric current flowing.

Overhead And Underground Cables

The main advantages and disadvantages of using overhead and underground cables for transmitting electricity are ...

COST: Overhead cables are at least 15 times cheaper to install.
VISUAL IMPACT: Overhead cables are visually unattractive, especially in rural areas.
EFFECT ON AGRICULTURE: Overhead cables restrict activity under lines, while underground cables restrict activity into the ground.
EFFECT ON ECOLOGY: Overhead cables need land for towers. Impact of digging trenches for underground cables.

Fossil Fuels

Coal, oil and gas are energy resources which have formed over millions of years from the remains of living things. For this reason they are called FOSSIL FUELS.

COAL   **OIL**   **GAS**

However, because these energy resources take so long to form, we are using them up at a far faster rate than they can be replaced, therefore reserves are dwindling and they will eventually run out. However, this does not deter us from generating most of our electricity using these resources.

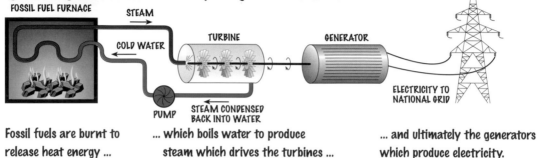

FOSSIL FUEL FURNACE — STEAM — COLD WATER — TURBINE — GENERATOR — ELECTRICITY TO NATIONAL GRID — PUMP — STEAM CONDENSED BACK INTO WATER

Fossil fuels are burnt to release heat energy ...   ... which boils water to produce steam which drives the turbines ...   ... and ultimately the generators which produce electricity.

This can be represented by the following energy chain.

CHEMICAL ENERGY → FURNACE → HEAT ENERGY → BOILER → POTENTIAL ENERGY → TURBINE → KINETIC ENERGY → GENERATOR → ELECTRICAL ENERGY

At each stage of the chain, energy is transferred to the surroundings in a 'non-useful' form, usually as heat. With so many stages in the production of electricity this does have implications for the environment as a power station has an efficiency of about 30%.

Wind And Water

These are energy resources which will not run out and are continually being replaced. They can be used in the generation of electricity where the energy resource is used to drive the turbine etc., and so unlike the fossil fuels there is no nasty burning involved.

WIND

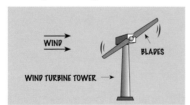

WIND — BLADES — WIND TURBINE TOWER

The force of the wind turns the blades of a wind turbine which in turn causes a generator to spin and produce electricity.

WATER

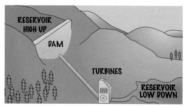

RESERVOIR HIGH UP — DAM — TURBINES — RESERVOIR LOW DOWN

Water stored in reservoirs above the power station is allowed to flow down through pipes to drive the turbines. The water can be pumped back up again when the demand for electricity is low.

KINETIC ENERGY → TURBINE → KINETIC ENERGY → GENERATOR → ELECTRICAL ENERGY

KINETIC ENERGY → TURBINE → KINETIC ENERGY → GENERATOR → ELECTRICAL ENERGY

With so few stages, these are fairly efficient ways of generating electricity compared to a fossil fuel power station.

Solar Heating Systems And Solar Cells

MATT BLACK SOLAR PANELS — WATER PIPE

Solar heating systems eg. solar panels, transfer sunlight directly into heat.

LIGHT ENERGY → SOLAR PANEL → HEAT ENERGY

Solar cells transfer sunlight directly into electricity.

LIGHT ENERGY → SOLAR CELL → ELECTRICAL ENERGY

HIGHER TIER

NON-RENEWABLE ENERGY RESOURCES are those which will **ONE DAY RUN OUT** and once they have been used they **CANNOT BE USED AGAIN.**

The four energy sources listed below are used to provide most of the electricity we need in this country directly through power stations. Some of the advantages and disadvantages of each one are listed below ...

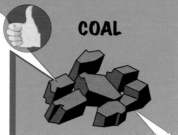

COAL

- Coal is relatively cheap and sometimes easy to obtain.
- Coal-fired power stations are flexible in meeting demand and have a quicker start-up time than their nuclear equivalents.
- Estimates suggest that there may be over a century's worth of coal left.

- Burning produces carbon dioxide (CO_2) and sulphur dioxide (SO_2).
- CO_2 causes 'global warming' due to the Greenhouse Effect.
- Coal produces more CO_2 per unit of energy produced than oil or gas.
- SO_2 causes acid rain unless ...
  ... the sulphur is removed before burning ...
  ... or the SO_2 is removed from the waste gases. Both of these add to the cost.

OIL

- There is plenty of oil left in the short to medium term. (30yrs?)
- The price is often variable but it can be relatively easy to find.
- Oil-fired power stations are flexible in meeting demand and have a quicker start-up time than both nuclear-powered and coal-fired reactors.

- Burning produces carbon dioxide and sulphur dioxide.
- CO_2 causes 'global warming' due to the Greenhouse Effect.
- Oil produces more CO_2 than gas, per unit of energy produced.
- SO_2 causes acid rain (see coal above).
- Oil is often carried between continents on tankers leading to the risk of spillage and pollution.

NATURAL GAS

- There is plenty of natural gas left in the short to medium term. (30 yrs?)
- As relatively easy to find as oil.
- Gas-fired power stations are flexible in meeting demand and have a quicker start-up time than nuclear, coal and oil.
- No sulphur dioxide (SO_2) is produced.

- Burning produces carbon dioxide (CO_2) although it is less than both coal and oil, per unit of energy produced.
- CO_2 causes 'global warming' due to the Greenhouse Effect.
- Expensive pipelines and networks are often required to transport it to the point of use.

NUCLEAR

- The cost and rate of use of fuel is relatively low.
- They can often be situated in sparsely populated areas (and should be!)
- Nuclear power stations are flexible in meeting demand.
- They <u>don't</u> produce carbon dioxide and sulphur dioxide.

- Although there is very little escape of radioactive material in normal use, radioactive waste can stay dangerously radioactive for thousands of years and safe storage is expensive.
- The cost of building and de-commissioning adds heavily to the unit cost of energy produced.
- They have the longest start-up time compared to coal, oil and gas.

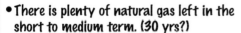
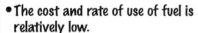

Summary

ADVANTAGES
- Produce huge amounts of energy.
- They are reliable.
- They are flexible in meeting demand.
- They don't take up much space (relatively).

DISADVANTAGES
- They pollute the environment.
- They cause 'global warming' and acid rain.
- They will 'soon' run out.
- Fuels may have to be transported long distances.

RENEWABLE ENERGY RESOURCES are those that WILL NOT RUN OUT, because they are CONTINUALLY BEING REPLACED. This is because many of them are 'powered' by the sun. For instance, the sun causes evaporation which results in rain and flowing water. It causes convection currents which result in winds and these winds cause waves. Tidal energy however, relies on the gravitational pull of the moon!

The four energy sources listed below represent the attempts of modern technology to provide us with a clean, safe alternative source of energy. Some of the advantages and disadvantages of each one are listed below ...

WIND

- Wind turbines don't require any fuel and need very little maintenance.
- They don't produce any pollutant gases such as carbon dioxide and sulphur dioxide.
- Once they're built they give 'free' energy when the wind is blowing.

- You need loads of them usually on hills and coastal areas and this can look a bit ugly (visual pollution). Also, noise can be a problem.
- Electricity output depends entirely on the strength of the wind.
- Not very flexible in meeting demand unless the energy is stored.
- Capital outlay can be high in building them.

HYDRO-ELECTRIC

- No fuel is required unless they are operated in reverse to store energy.
- Very fast start-up time to meet sudden increases in demand.
- Large amounts of clean, reliable electricity can be produced.
- When operated in reverse, by pumping water into the higher reservoir, surplus electricity can be stored to help meet future peak demand.

- Location is critical and often involves damming upland valleys which means flooding farms, forests and natural habitats.
- To actually achieve a net output (aside from pumping) there must be adequate rainfall in the region where the reservoir is.
- Very high initial capital outlay - but worth the investment in the end.

TIDAL

- No fuel is required.
- They don't produce any pollutant gases such as carbon dioxide and sulphur dioxide.
- Once they're built they provide 'free' energy - at certain times!
- Barrage water can be released when demand for electricity is high.

- Tidal barrages, across estuaries, are unsightly, a hazard to shipping, and destroy the habitats of wading birds etc.
- Output depends on daily variations in the state of the tide and monthly and annual variations in its height.
- High initial capital outlay in building them.

WAVES

- No fuel is required.
- They don't produce any pollutant gases such as carbon dioxide and sulphur dioxide.
- Once they're built they provide 'free' energy - at certain times!

- Output depends on the energy contained in the waves.
- For a decent amount of energy you would need thousands of them.
- High initial capital output in building them.

Summary

ADVANTAGES
- No fuel costs during operation.
- No chemical pollution.
- Often low maintenance.
- Don't contribute to 'global warming' and acid rain.

DISADVANTAGES
- With the exception of hydro-electric they produce small amounts of electricity.
- Take up lots of space and are unsightly.
- Unreliable (apart form H-E), weather dependent and can't match demand.
- High initial capital outlay.

Use Of Low Energy Appliances

When appliances transfer energy, only part of it is USEFULLY TRANSFERRED to where it is wanted and in the form it is wanted in. The remainder is transferred in some non-useful way and is therefore 'wasted'. Low energy appliances are more efficient at transferring energy in the form required which means that they need a smaller energy input compared to a less efficient appliance.

If we compare a low energy light bulb and an ordinary tungsten filament light bulb ...

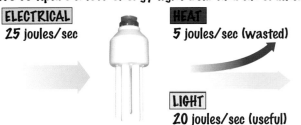

ELECTRICAL
25 joules/sec

HEAT
5 joules/sec (wasted)

LIGHT
20 joules/sec (useful)

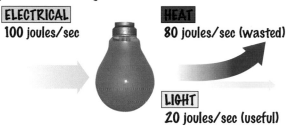

ELECTRICAL
100 joules/sec

HEAT
80 joules/sec (wasted)

LIGHT
20 joules/sec (useful)

... both produce the same amount of useful energy every second but there is a great difference in the amount of energy input into both appliances!

Use Of Insulation

The transfer of energy between objects at different temperatures can be reduced by the use of insulation.

 A hot water tank is insulated to reduce the transfer of heat energy from inside the tank to its outside.

 A refrigerator is insulated to reduce the transfer of heat energy from outside the fridge to its inside.

Reducing Heat Losses From A Building

There are many different ways in which heat losses from a building can be reduced ...

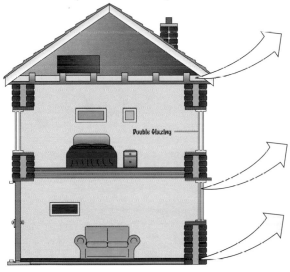

Double Glazing

LOFT INSULATION

Reduces heat loss by conduction and convection. Loft insulation has air (a good insulator) trapped between its fibres.

DOUBLE GLAZING

Reduces heat loss by conduction and convection. Double glazing has air trapped between its panes of glass.

CAVITY WALL INSULATION

Reduces heat loss by conduction and especially convection. Again it is an insulator that has air trapped in it.

HIGHER TIER

Many insulating materials, such as the loft insulation ...
... and cavity wall insulation above, ...
... have AIR trapped in them.
A consequence of this is that the air ...
... is NOT FREE TO FORM CONVECTION CURRENTS ...
... which would otherwise result in HEAT ENERGY ...
... being lost.

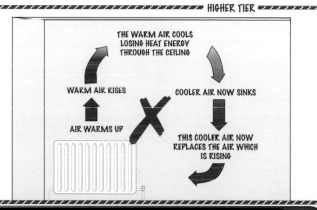

THE WARM AIR COOLS LOSING HEAT ENERGY THROUGH THE CEILING

WARM AIR RISES

COOLER AIR NOW SINKS

AIR WARMS UP

THIS COOLER AIR NOW REPLACES THE AIR WHICH IS RISING

VOLTAGE, CURRENT AND RESISTANCE

The amount of current flowing through a component depends on ...
- ... the VOLTAGE across the component, and ...
- ... the RESISTANCE of the component.

VOLTAGE is measured by a VOLTMETER connected in parallel;
CURRENT is measured by an AMMETER connected in series.

STANDARD SYMBOLS

Switch (open)	Variable Resistor	Lamp	Voltmeter
Switch (closed)	Fuse	Diode	Ammeter
Cell	LDR	Resistor	Thermistor
Battery			

RESISTANCE ...

VOLTAGE (V) = CURRENT (A) x RESISTANCE (Ω)

$$\frac{V}{I \times R}$$

RESISTANCE OF COMPONENTS ...

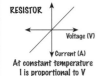

RESISTOR — Voltage (V) / Current (A)
At constant temperature I is proportional to V

FILAMENT LAMP — Voltage (V) / Current (A)
Resistance increases with temperature

DIODE — Voltage (V) / Current (A)
Current flows in one direction

- In LIGHT DEPENDENT RESISTORS resistance decreases as light increases.
- In THERMISTORS resistance decreases as temperature increases.

SERIES AND PARALLEL CIRCUITS

IN SERIES CIRCUITS ...

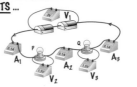
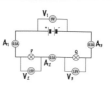

- The CURRENT is the SAME at any point in the circuit. $A_1 = A_2 = A_3$
- The VOLTAGE is shared between the components. $V_1 = V_2 + V_3$

IN PARALLEL CIRCUITS ...

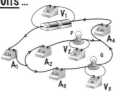
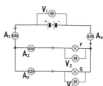

- TOTAL CURRENT in main circuit is equal to the sum of the currents passing through each component. $A_1 = A_2 + A_3 = A_4$
- The VOLTAGE across each component is the same. $V_1 = V_2 = V_3$
- The current through each component depends on its RESISTANCE.

MAINS ELECTRICITY

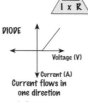

EARTH WIRE, FUSE, CASING, NEUTRAL WIRE, CABLE GRIP, LIVE WIRE, CABLE

ALTERNATING CURRENT   DIRECT CURRENT

- a.c. changes direction continuously (50Hz).
- d.c. one direction only. Cells and batteries.

FUSES ...

CURRENT LARGER THAN CURRENT RATING OF FUSE	→	FUSE BURNS OUT	→	CIRCUIT IS BROKEN	→	NO CURRENT FLOWS	→	CABLE OR APPLIANCE IS PROTECTED

INSULATION AND DOUBLE INSULATION

- Any current-carrying component should be separated from human contact by insulation.
- Some appliances are double insulated so that all metal parts inside cannot come into contact with the outside plastic case. eg. a hair drier. These appliances don't have an earth wire but do have a fuse.

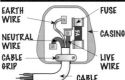

RESIDUAL CURRENT CIRCUIT BREAKER (RCCB)

These detect the current in the live and neutral conductors and immediately break the circuit if there is any imbalance between the two. Fast acting and easily re-settable.

GENERATING, DISTRIBUTING AND USING ELECTRICAL ENERGY

ENERGY TRANSFER AND COST

Energy from the mains supply is measured in kilowatt-hours (kWh).
In 1 hour, a 1 kilowatt iron transfer 1kWh of energy.

COST OF ELECTRICITY = POWER (kW) x TIME (h) x COST OF 1kWh

SAVING ENERGY

- Low energy appliances are more efficient.
- Insulators prevent heat loss.
- Air is used as an insulator when it is stopped from forming convection currents.

FIBREGLASS ROOF INSULATION, DOUBLE GLAZING, CAVITY WALL INSULATION

GENERATION OF ELECTRICITY

Generators basically rotate a magnet inside a coil of wire.

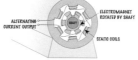
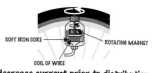

ALTERNATING CURRENT OUTPUT, ELECTROMAGNET ROTATED BY SHAFT, SHAFT, STATIC COILS

SOFT IRON CORE, ROTATING MAGNET, COIL OF WIRE

TRANSFORMERS ... step up voltage and decrease current prior to distribution which reduces energy loss. They then step down the voltage prior to domestic use.

- Overhead cables are cheaper but are visually unattractive.
- Agriculture can also be affected.

ANALYSIS OF NON-RENEWABLE ENERGY RESOURCES

These can be represented by the following energy chain ...

CHEMICAL ENERGY → (FURNACE) HEAT ENERGY → (BOILER) POT^N ENERGY → (TURBINE) KINETIC ENERGY → (GENERATOR) ELECTRICAL ENERGY →

... with the exception of NUCLEAR which produces heat by fission.

COAL +	COAL −
• Cheap, easy to obtain. • Flexible, quicker start-up time than nuclear. • A century's worth of coal left.	• Produces SO_2 and more CO_2 than oil or gas. • CO_2 causes 'global warming' • SO_2 causes acid rain; costs to remove it.
OIL +	**OIL −**
• Plenty left. • Relatively easy to find. • Flexible. • Quicker start-up than coal or nuclear.	• Produces SO_2 and more CO_2 than gas. • CO_2 causes 'global warming'. • SO_2 causes acid rain; costs to remove it. • Transportation risks spillage and pollution.
GAS +	**GAS −**
• Plenty left. • Relatively easy to find. • Flexible - quicker start-up time than nuclear, coal and oil. • No SO_2 produced.	• Produces CO_2 (less than coal and oil) • CO_2 causes 'global warming'. • Expensive pipelines and networks to point of use.
NUCLEAR +	**NUCLEAR −**
• Cost and rate of use is low. • Situated in sparsely populated areas. • Flexible in meeting demand. • DOESN'T produce CO_2 or SO_2.	• Waste is dangerous for thousands of years; safe storage is expensive. • Building and decommissioning is costly. • Longest start-up time of these four.

+	−
• Huge amounts of Energy • Reliable • Flexible • Compact	• Pollute Environment • Global warming and acid rain • Will soon run out • Transportation cost and dangers

ANALYSIS OF RENEWABLE ENERGY RESOURCES

These can be represented by the following energy chain ...

KINETIC ENERGY → (TURBINE) KINETIC ENERGY → (GENERATOR) ELECTRICAL ENERGY →

WIND +	WIND −
• Require no fuel and little maintenance. • Doesn't produce any CO_2 or SO_2. • Once built, energy is free.	• Need lots; visual and noise pollution. • Output depends on strength of wind. • Not very flexible. • High capital outlay.
TIDAL & WAVES +	**TIDAL & WAVES −**
• No fuel required. • Don't produce CO_2 or SO_2. • Once built energy is free. • High demand - release barrage water.	• Unsightly tidal barrages, destroy habitats. • Daily variations affect output. • High capital outlay.
HYDRO-ELECTRIC +	**HYDRO-ELECTRIC −**
• No fuel required unless storing energy, to meet future peak demand. • Fast start-up time. • Produces large amounts; clean; reliable.	• Farms, forests and natural habitats may be flooded when damming. • Rainfall must be adequate. • Very high capital outlay.

+	−
• No fuel costs • No chemical pollution • Low maintenance • No global warming or acid rain	• Only H.E produces much energy • Unsightly - take up space • Unreliable - weather dependant • High capital outlay

Waves are ...
* ... a REGULAR PATTERN OF DISTURBANCE ...
* ... which TRANSFERS ENERGY from one point to another WITHOUT ANY TRANSFER OF MATTER.
* Waves can be produced in ROPES, SPRINGS and on the SURFACE OF WATER.

Features Of Waves

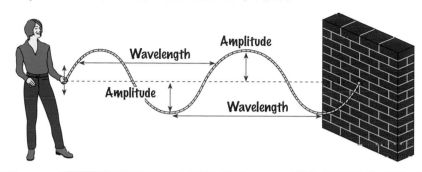

A wave can be generated by simply tying one end of a rope to a wall ...

AMPLITUDE is ...	WAVELENGTH is ...	FREQUENCY is ...
... the MAXIMUM DISTURBANCE caused by a wave.	... the DISTANCE BETWEEN CORRESPONDING POINTS ON TWO SUCCESSIVE DISTURBANCES.	... the NUMBER of WAVES PRODUCED, (or passing a particular point) IN ONE SECOND.

Waves of a different amplitude, wavelength and frequency can be generated using a signal generator connected to an oscilloscope which displays a representation of the wave on its screen.

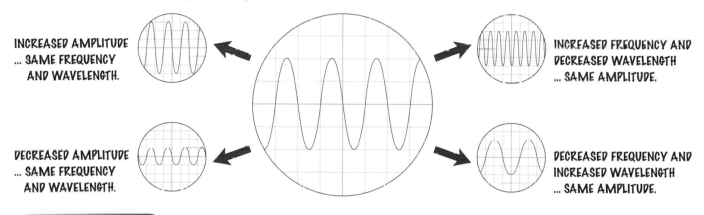

INCREASED AMPLITUDE ... SAME FREQUENCY AND WAVELENGTH.

INCREASED FREQUENCY AND DECREASED WAVELENGTH ... SAME AMPLITUDE.

DECREASED AMPLITUDE ... SAME FREQUENCY AND WAVELENGTH.

DECREASED FREQUENCY AND INCREASED WAVELENGTH ... SAME AMPLITUDE.

Types Of Wave

There are TWO types of wave, both of which can be shown using a SLINKY SPRING.

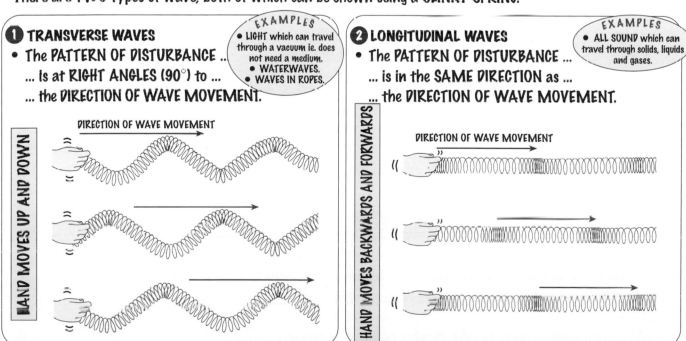

❶ TRANSVERSE WAVES
* The PATTERN OF DISTURBANCE ...
  ... is at RIGHT ANGLES (90°) to ...
  ... the DIRECTION OF WAVE MOVEMENT.

EXAMPLES
* LIGHT which can travel through a vacuum ie. does not need a medium.
* WATERWAVES.
* WAVES IN ROPES.

DIRECTION OF WAVE MOVEMENT

HAND MOVES UP AND DOWN

❷ LONGITUDINAL WAVES
* The PATTERN OF DISTURBANCE ...
  ... is in the SAME DIRECTION as ...
  ... the DIRECTION OF WAVE MOVEMENT.

EXAMPLES
* ALL SOUND which can travel through solids, liquids and gases.

DIRECTION OF WAVE MOVEMENT

HAND MOVES BACKWARDS AND FORWARDS

LIGHT is part of a 'family' called the ELECTROMAGNETIC SPECTRUM. The other 'family members' form a CONTINUOUS SPECTRUM which extends beyond each end of the visible spectrum produced by light.

Each type of electromagnetic radiation ...

① TRAVELS AT THE SAME SPEED (300,000,000 m/s) THROUGH SPACE (a vacuum), as a TRANSVERSE WAVE.

② Has a DIFFERENT WAVELENGTH and a DIFFERENT FREQUENCY. The energy associated with the radiation, and thus its potential danger, increases with increasing frequency.

LOW FREQUENCY LONG WAVELENGTH

RADIO WAVES

- Broadcasting of Radio and TV programmes between different places. The longer wavelength radio waves are reflected from the ionosphere, an electrically charged layer in the Earth's upper atmosphere. • Communications, including satellite transmissions.

MICROWAVES

- Communications, including satellite transmissions as they pass easily through the Earth's atmosphere.
  - Cooking; they are absorbed by water molecules, causing them to heat up.

INFRA-RED

- Grills • Night vision • Remote controls
- Security systems • Treatment of muscular problems

WHITE LIGHT is made up of many different colours (Red, Orange, Yellow, Green, Blue, Indigo and Violet) which are refracted by different amounts as they pass through the prism to give us a spectrum of colours.
Uses: • Vision • Photography

WHITE LIGHT — GLASS PRISM

VISIBLE LIGHT

ULTRA VIOLET

- Sunbeds • Detecting forged bank notes.
- Fluorescent lamps and security coding where a surface coated with special paint absorbs U-V and emits LIGHT.

X-RAYS

- Observing the internal structure of objects and materials including the human body.

GAMMA RAYS

- Sterilising food and medical equipment • Treatment of cancers

HIGH FREQUENCY SHORT WAVELENGTH

Effect Of Electromagnetic Radiation On The Human Body

Excessive exposure can have serious consequences for the human body ...
MICROWAVES - absorbed by water in cells causing internal heating of body tissues.
INFRA-RED - absorbed by skin and felt as heat, possibly resulting in skin burns.
ULTRA VIOLET - can cause damage to the eyes and surface cells, possibly resulting in skin cancer.
X-RAYS - can cause damage to cells, possibly resulting in cancer.

Refraction Of Light

Light changes direction when it crosses a boundary between two transparent materials (media) of different densities - UNLESS it meets the boundary at an angle of 90° (along a NORMAL).

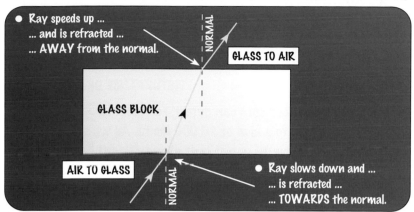

- Ray speeds up ...
  ... and is refracted ...
  ... AWAY from the normal.

GLASS TO AIR

NORMAL

GLASS BLOCK

AIR TO GLASS

NORMAL

- Ray slows down and ...
  ... is refracted ...
  ... TOWARDS the normal.

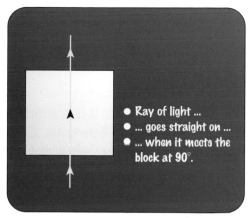

- Ray of light ...
- ... goes straight on ...
- ... when it meets the block at 90°.

Optical Fibres

An optical fibre is a LONG, FLEXIBLE, TRANSPARENT CABLE of very small diameter. As light or infra-red radiation travels down an optical fibre it is NOT refracted but internally reflected along its length because the glass/air boundary acts like a plane mirror.

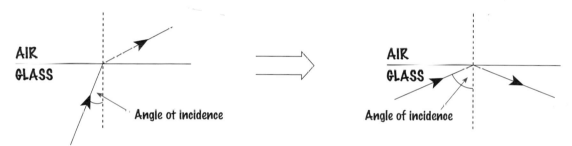

AIR
GLASS

Angle of incidence

AIR
GLASS

Angle of incidence

Normally a ray of light or infra-red passes from glass into air and is refracted away from the normal. This happens if the angle of incidence is below a certain value.

However, if the angle of incidence is beyond a certain value the ray of light or infra-red is internally reflected and not refracted. This is what happens inside an optical fibre.

The great advantage of optical fibres is that they can be used to transmit information with little energy loss resulting in less weakening of the information signal.

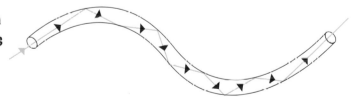

Analogue And Digital Signals

- Analogue signals vary continually in amplitude and/or frequency. They are very similar to the sound waves of speech or music.
- Digital signals on the other hand do not vary and they have only two states, ON(1) or OFF(0). There are no inbetween states. The information is a series of pulses.

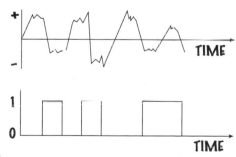

+

−

TIME

1

0

TIME

The advantages of using digital signals instead of analogue signals are ...
- Better quality, with no change in the signal information during transmission.
- More information can be transmitted in a given time.

Sound

- Sound is produced when something VIBRATES backwards and forwards. As we have already seen sound travels as a LONGITUDINAL WAVE.

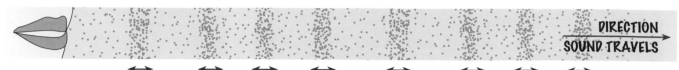

DIRECTION SOUND TRAVELS

DISTURBANCE OF AIR MOLECULES

A sound can be heard if it is within the AUDIBLE RANGE that our ears can detect. For most adults this range goes from a low of 20 Hertz (ie. 20 vibrations every second) up to a high of 20,000 Hertz. As we get older though, this upper limit does decrease. Some children, however, may have an upper limit above 20,000 Hertz.

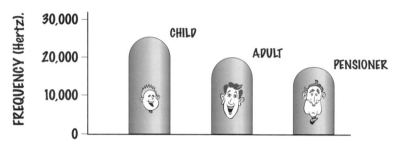

Ultrasound

These are SOUND WAVES of FREQUENCIES GREATER than 20,000 Hertz ie. above the UPPER LIMIT of the HEARING RANGE for most HUMANS. They are made by ELECTRONIC SYSTEMS which produce ELECTRICAL OSCILLATIONS which are used to generate the ULTRASONIC WAVES.

They have many uses ...

① Medical Imaging

Ultrasonic waves can be used to produce a visual image of different structures found in the body such as the heart, liver, kidneys, breast and large blood vessels. Any problems can be detected without the patient having to undergo any unnecessary surgery.

Another important use of ultrasound waves is pre-natal scanning ...

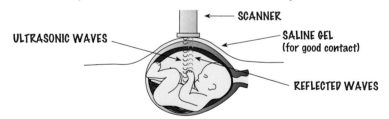

THIS METHOD CAN BE USED TO DETERMINE SIZE, POSITION AND ANY ABNORMALITIES. IT IS SAFE, WITH NO RISK TO PATIENT OR BABY.

- Ultrasonic waves are sent into the BODY by the SCANNER which is placed in GOOD CONTACT WITH THE SKIN.
- The ultrasonic waves are PARTLY REFLECTED at any SURFACES or BOUNDARIES ...
- ... within the body which have a DIFFERENT DENSITY or STRUCTURE.
- The TIME TAKEN for these REFLECTIONS is a ...
- ... measure of the DEPTH of the REFLECTING SURFACE.
- The reflected waves are usually PROCESSED to produce a VISUAL IMAGE on a screen.

② Echo Sounding

- Ultrasonic waves are sent out from the BOTTOM of the SHIP.
- The TIME DELAY of the REFLECTIONS can ...
- ... be used to CALCULATE the DEPTH of the WATER.
- This method can also be used for locating submarines...
- ... and shoals of fish.

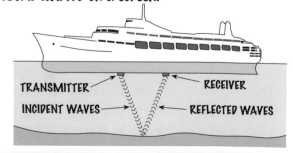

This page is similar to work covered in module 3, but there are important differences.

The Atom

The ATOM consists of a small CENTRAL NUCLEUS made up of PROTONS and NEUTRONS (one exception) ...
... surrounded by ELECTRONS arranged in SHELLS. A simple example - Helium

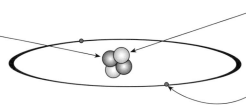

PROTON
- Positively charged.
- An atom has the same number of protons as electrons ...
... so the atom as a whole has no electrical charge.
- Same mass as a neutron.

NEUTRON
- Neutral - no charge.
- Same mass as a proton.

ELECTRON
- Negatively charged.
- Same number of electrons as protons.
- Mass negligible ie. nearly nothing!

ATOMIC PARTICLE	RELATIVE MASS	RELATIVE CHARGE
PROTON	1	+1
NEUTRON	1	0
ELECTRON	1/1840 (almost nothing)	-1

Mass Number And Atomic Number

Atoms of an element can be described very conveniently; take the Helium atom above ...

MASS NUMBER (Nucleon Number)
NUMBER OF PROTONS AND NEUTRONS.

ATOMIC NUMBER (Proton Number)
NUMBER OF PROTONS.

$$_2^4 He$$

ELEMENT SYMBOL
IN THIS CASE, THE ELEMENT HELIUM.

Here are some more elements in the periodic table.

ELEMENT	HYDROGEN	BORON	OXYGEN	ZINC	GOLD
SYMBOL	$_1^1 H$	$_5^{11} B$	$_8^{16} O$	$_{30}^{64} Zn$	$_{79}^{197} Au$
MASS NUMBER	1	11	16	64	197
ATOMIC NUMBER	1	5	8	30	79
No. of PROTONS	1	5	8	30	79
No. of NEUTRONS	0 (the exception)	6	8	34	118
No. of ELECTRONS	1	5	8	30	79

ALWAYS THE SAME!

Isotopes

- ALL ATOMS of a particular ELEMENT have the SAME NUMBER OF PROTONS.
- The NUMBER of PROTONS, DEFINES THE ELEMENT.
  - HOWEVER, some atoms of the SAME ELEMENT can have DIFFERENT NUMBERS OF NEUTRONS ...
    - ... these are called ISOTOPES.

Example:

Oxygen has 3 isotopes ...

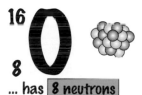

$_8^{16} O$ ... has 8 neutrons

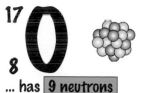

$_8^{17} O$ ... has 9 neutrons

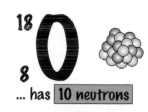

$_8^{18} O$ ... has 10 neutrons

Radioactive Decay

Some substances contain ISOTOPES of ATOMS with UNSTABLE NUCLEI which may split up or DISINTEGRATE emitting RADIATION. The atoms of such isotopes disintegrate randomly and are said to be RADIOACTIVE.

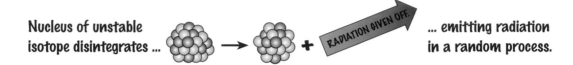

Nucleus of unstable isotope disintegrates ...   + RADIATION GIVEN OFF.   ... emitting radiation in a random process.

The Three Types Of Radiation

A radioactive substance is capable of emitting one of the following types of radiation, ALPHA, BETA or GAMMA. A simple way to distinguish between them is through their ability to be absorbed by different types of material.

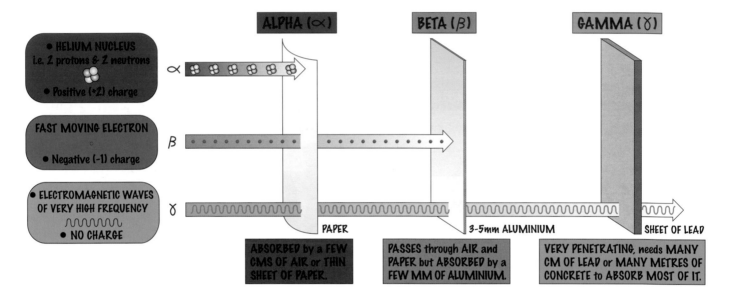

- HELIUM NUCLEUS i.e. 2 protons & 2 neutrons
- Positive (+2) charge

FAST MOVING ELECTRON
- Negative (-1) charge

- ELECTROMAGNETIC WAVES OF VERY HIGH FREQUENCY
- NO CHARGE

ALPHA (α)   BETA (β)   GAMMA (γ)

PAPER   3-5mm ALUMINIUM   SHEET OF LEAD

ABSORBED by a FEW CMS OF AIR or THIN SHEET OF PAPER.   PASSES through AIR and PAPER but ABSORBED by a FEW MM OF ALUMINIUM.   VERY PENETRATING, needs MANY CM OF LEAD or MANY METRES OF CONCRETE to ABSORB MOST OF IT.

Background Radiation

This is RADIATION THAT OCCURS NATURALLY ALL AROUND US. It only provides a very small dose so there's no danger to our health.

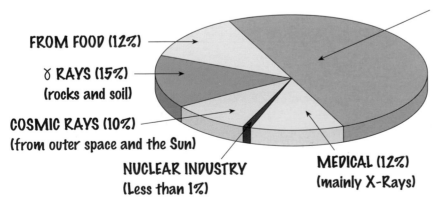

FROM FOOD (12%)

γ RAYS (15%) (rocks and soil)

COSMIC RAYS (10%) (from outer space and the Sun)

NUCLEAR INDUSTRY (Less than 1%)

MEDICAL (12%) (mainly X-Rays)

RADON GAS (50%)
(A colourless and odourless gas produced during the radioactive decay of uranium which is found naturally in granite rock. Released at the surface of the ground it does pose a threat if it builds up in a home eg. it can result in lung cancer. Areas of the country at most risk are Devon and Cornwall.)

13% are MAN MADE SOURCES.   87% are NATURAL SOURCES.

Ionisation

- When RADIATION COLLIDES with NEUTRAL ATOMS or MOLECULES they may become CHARGED due to electrons being 'knocked out' of their structure. This alters their structure leaving them as IONS or CHARGED PARTICLES.

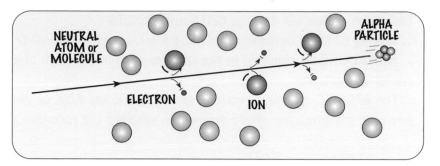

- ALPHA, BETA and GAMMA radiation are therefore known as IONISING RADIATION ...
  ... and can damage 'healthy' MOLECULES in LIVING CELLS resulting in death of the cell.

Uses Of Radiation

(1) Controlling the thickness of sheet materials

- When radiation passes through a material ...
  ... SOME OF IT is ABSORBED by the MATERIAL.
  The GREATER the THICKNESS of the material, the GREATER the ABSORPTION of radiation.
  This idea can be used to control the thickness of different manufactured materials, eg. in a PAPER MILL ...

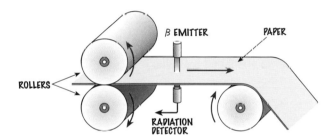

- If paper thickness is too great ...
- ... then more radiation is absorbed and ...
- ... less passes through to the detector.
- This causes a signal to be sent to the rollers ...
- ... which move closer together etc.

A β emitter is used since the paper would absorb $\propto$ particles and would have no effect at all on γ rays, regardless of its thickness.

(2) Smoke detectors

- Most smoke alarms contain americium-241 ...
  ... which is an $\propto$ emitter.
- Emitted $\propto$ particles cause ionisation of the air particles ...
  ... and the ions formed are attracted to the oppositely charged electrodes.
- This results in a current flowing in the circuit.
- When smoke enters the space between the two electrodes ...
  ... less ionisation takes place ...
  ... as the $\propto$ particles are absorbed by the smoke particles.
- A smaller current than normal now flows and the alarm sounds.

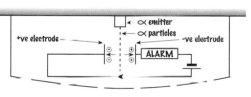

(3) Sterilisation of medical instruments

- GAMMA RAYS can be used ...
  ... to STERILISE MEDICAL INSTRUMENTS ...
  ... because germs and bacteria are destroyed by them.
- An advantage of this method ...
  ... is that no heat is required, therefore ...
  ... minimising damage to instruments.

Effect Of Ionising Radiation On Living Organisms

Ionising radiation can damage CELLS and TISSUES ...

... causing CANCER including LEUKAEMIA (cancer of the blood) or ...

... MUTATIONS (ie. changes) in the cells resulting in the birth of deformed babies in future generations.

As for all radiation ...

... The GREATER the DOSE received, the GREATER the RISK of DAMAGE.

However the damaging effect depends on whether the radiation source is OUTSIDE or INSIDE the body.

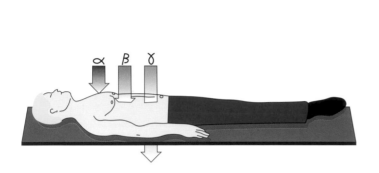

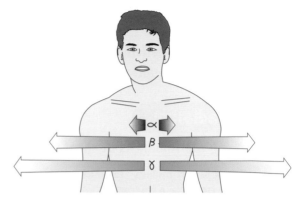

If the source is OUTSIDE ...
- ∝ CANNOT PENETRATE INTO THE BODY and is stopped by the skin.
- β and γ CAN PENETRATE INTO THE BODY to reach the CELLS of ORGANS and be absorbed by them.

If the source is INSIDE ...
- ∝ causes MOST DAMAGE as it is STRONGLY ABSORBED BY CELLS causing the MOST IONISATION.
- β and γ cause LESS DAMAGE as they are less likely to be absorbed by cells.

Disposal Of Radioactive Waste

Radioactive isotopes are used in the Nuclear Fuel Industry to generate electricity cleanly and efficiently. However, there is a problem with disposal of waste. This is due to the fact that the waste products are still radioactive and will remain so for possibly thousands of years.

This means that there is a duty of care to prevent the environment becoming contaminated resulting in damage to people's health. Waste is categorised into low level, intermediate level and high level waste, and dealt with accordingly.

- The key to management of radioactive waste is to IMMOBILISE it, ie. change it into a form that limits the ability of radionuclides to escape into the environment.

- Liquid high level waste is immobilised by mixing with glass making ingredients, melting it and pouring the glass into stainless steel containers.

- Intermediate level wastes are immobilised in cement in stainless steel drums.

- The immobilised wastes are then kept in stores next to the treatment plant.

- Low level waste is disposed of at Drigg in Cumbria.

*Many thanks to NIREX for permission to reproduce this photograph.

GRAVITY is an attractive force which affects everything from the falling down of apples from trees to the motion of the planets around the Sun. The MASS of an object is the amount of matter that it contains. On Earth an object of MASS 1 kg experiences a downward pull force, or has a WEIGHT of 10 NEWTONS (N) ie. the weight of an object on Earth in newtons (N) is always 10 TIMES GREATER than its mass in kilograms. This value of 10 NEWTONS PER KILOGRAM is a constant for all objects on Earth and is called the GRAVITATIONAL FIELD STRENGTH.

Weight, mass and gravitational field strength are related by the equation.

WEIGHT (N) = MASS (kg) x GRAVITATIONAL FIELD STRENGTH (N/kg)

Examples

① Calculate the weight of an object on Earth if it has a mass of 2000grams and g = 10N/kg.
Using the equation: WEIGHT = MASS x GRAVITATIONAL FIELD STRENGTH
= 2kg   x 10N/kg
= 20N

MASS MUST BE IN KILOGRAMS

② Calculate the mass of an object on Earth if it has a weight of 234N and g = 10N/kg.
Using the equation:
(rearranged using our formula triangle.)

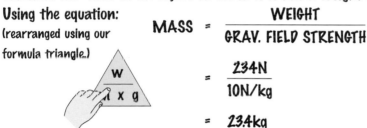

$$MASS = \frac{WEIGHT}{GRAV.\ FIELD\ STRENGTH}$$

$$= \frac{234N}{10N/kg}$$

$$= 23.4kg$$

However, on the MOON or a DIFFERENT PLANET the SAME OBJECT would have the SAME MASS but a DIFFERENT WEIGHT! For example if we take an object with a mass of 1kg.

• On the Moon its weight would be about 1.6N; this is ONE SIXTH its value on Earth. This is because the Moon has a smaller mass than the Earth and 'g' on the Moon is ONE SIXTH its value on Earth.

• On JUPITER its weight would be about 26N which is over two and a half times its value on Earth. This is because it has a bigger mass than the Earth and 'g' on Jupiter is 2.6 times its value on Earth.

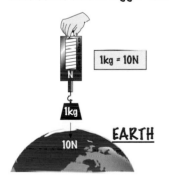

EARTH
1kg = 10N
1kg
10N

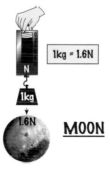

MOON
1kg = 1.6N
1kg
1.6N

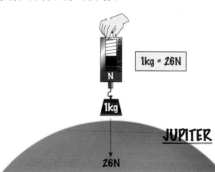

JUPITER
1kg = 26N
1kg
26N

In summary ...
... on EARTH

Mass (kg)	Weight (N)
1	10
2	20
5	50
10	100

... on the MOON

Mass (kg)	Weight (N)
1	1.6
2	3.2
5	8
10	16

... on JUPITER

Mass (kg)	Weight (N)
1	26
2	52
5	130
10	260

A SATELLITE is an OBJECT which is in orbit around a LARGER OBJECT.

The smaller object stays in its orbit because the larger object exerts an INWARD PULL FORCE on it.

If you swing a rubber ball attached to a piece of string in a horizontal circle then the inward force that keeps the ball moving in its circular orbit is provided by the tension force in the string.

TENSION FORCE

As you swing the ball you can feel this tension which is keeping the ball moving in its orbit.

The same principle can be applied to objects in the solar system.

... PLANETS ORBIT the SUN

... the MOON and ARTIFICIAL SATELLITES ORBIT the EARTH

... COMETS ORBIT the SUN

All of these stay in their orbit because of the force of gravity acting between the two objects.

Natural Satellites Of The Sun

The PLANETS are kept in their orbit by the VERY LARGE GRAVITATIONAL FIELD of the Sun.

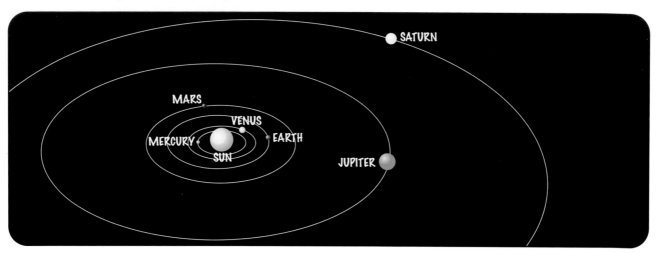

If the gravitational force of the Sun was to suddenly disappear then the Earth and other planets would go flying off into space (in a straight line!).

Satellites Of The Earth

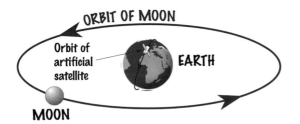

ORBIT OF MOON

Orbit of artificial satellite

EARTH

MOON

The MOON and ARTIFICIAL SATELLITES are kept in their orbit by the INWARD GRAVITATIONAL FORCE of the Earth. The Sun also influences the Moon's orbit but to a much lesser extent because the Earth is much closer to the Moon than the Sun.

Remember, that some other planets also have moons, eg. Europa is a moon of Jupiter. Again these are kept in their orbit by the gravitational force of the planet they orbit.

Comets

Comets have a core of frozen gas and dust. They orbit the sun with a very elliptical orbit which brings them near to the sun before taking them far off to the limits of the solar system. As they approach the sun, gases evaporate to form the tail making the comet easy to see.

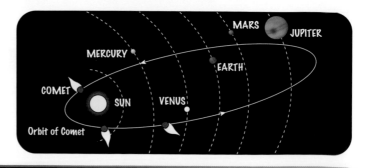

Stars, Galaxies And The Universe

- Our SUN is ONE STAR out of the many millions of stars in OUR GALAXY, THE MILKY WAY.
- The Milky Way is ONE GALAXY out of at least a billion galaxies in the UNIVERSE.

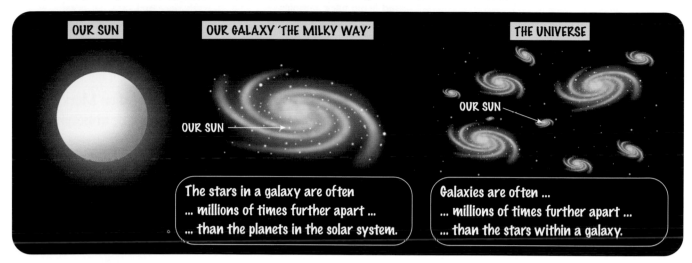

OUR SUN

OUR GALAXY 'THE MILKY WAY'

OUR SUN

THE UNIVERSE

OUR SUN

The stars in a galaxy are often ...
... millions of times further apart ...
... than the planets in the solar system.

Galaxies are often ...
... millions of times further apart ...
... than the stars within a galaxy.

Formation Of Stars

STARS, including our Sun are formed when GRAVITATIONAL FORCES cause a NEBULA (a cloud of gas and dust) to collapse. This generates heat and eventually nuclear reactions take place releasing massive amounts of energy.

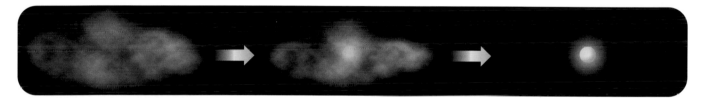

Life Cycle Of A Star

When a star is in its stable period (like our sun) it is called a MAIN SEQUENCE STAR. During this period ...
... the MASSIVE FORCES OF ATTRACTION pulling INWARDS ...
... are BALANCED by FORCES ACTING OUTWARDS which are created by the HUGE TEMPERATURES within the star.
Eventually, the supply of HYDROGEN runs out and the star SWELLS UP becoming colder and colder ...

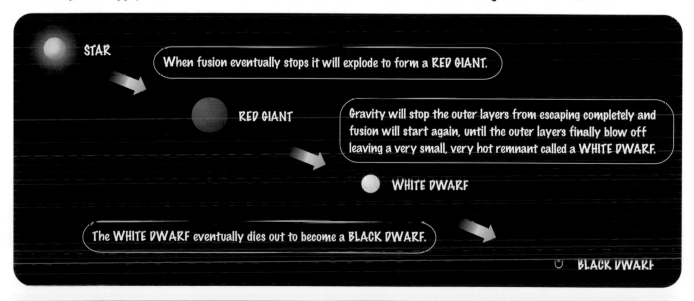

STAR

When fusion eventually stops it will explode to form a RED GIANT.

RED GIANT

Gravity will stop the outer layers from escaping completely and fusion will start again, until the outer layers finally blow off leaving a very small, very hot remnant called a WHITE DWARF.

WHITE DWARF

The WHITE DWARF eventually dies out to become a BLACK DWARF.

BLACK DWARF

Amongst the prime contenders for life in our solar system are MARS and EUROPA (one of Jupiter's satellites). However this life may be fairly basic, such as microbes etc. or their fossilised remains. There are many ways of obtaining evidence that life exists ...

Actually travel to Mars or Europa and look for signs of life!	Use robots to travel to Mars or Europa and bring back samples.	Use robots to travel to Mars or Europa and take pictures!

Could take many months to get there.	Not as reliable as humans!	Pictures might not come out!

In 1975, the US launched two unmanned spacecraft, Viking 1 and 2, to find out if life existed on Mars. They released landers which were used to take photographs of the surface and to analyse the atmosphere and soil. This analysis can take various forms ...

Detecting changes produced by living things ...
The samples of rock or dust can be placed inside a sealed container whose atmosphere has been accurately analysed. Over a period of time the atmosphere is checked to see if there are changes which have occurred which cannot be attributed to chemical or geological processes eg. oxygen could have been used up or produced by living things in the sample.

Of course it's possible that there may be highly advanced forms of life elsewhere in the universe and these may be detected using radio telescopes to try to find meaningful signals in a narrow waveband against the background 'noise' of the universe. The SEARCH FOR EXTRA-TERRESTRIAL INTELLIGENCE (SETI) has now gone on for more than 40 years without success; but remember the universe is vast and any day now ...

Origin And Future Of The Universe   There have been many theories ...

- The 'STEADY STATE' theory was that the Universe had always existed and will exist for ever. One drawback to this theory is that the light from every star in the sky (and there are billions of them) would now be reaching us continuously. A consequence of this is that the night sky would be completely lit up which it isn't! Today this theory is rejected in favour of ...

- The 'BIG BANG' theory which states that the whole universe is expanding and that it all started billions of years ago in one place with a huge explosion ie. the big bang!

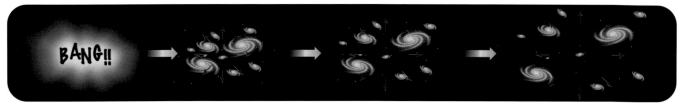

However, the future of the Universe does depend on the amount of mass present. If there is not enough mass present the Universe will keep on expanding for ever and ever. If there is enough mass present GRAVITY will take its effect causing the Universe to stop expanding and to start collapsing!

HIGHER TIER

Evidence For The Origin Of The Universe

If a SOURCE OF LIGHT (same effect occurs with sound) moves away from us the wavelengths of the light in its spectrum are LONGER than if the source was not moving!!! For light this is known as 'RED-SHIFT' as the wavelengths are 'shifted' TOWARDS THE RED END OF THE SPECTRUM.

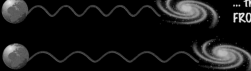

The wavelengths of light from other galaxies are longer than expected, which means that ...	... the GALAXY IS MOVING AWAY FROM US VERY QUICKLY ...
... this effect is exaggerated in galaxies which are further away, which means that ...	... the FURTHER AWAY A GALAXY IS, THE FASTER IT IS MOVING AWAY FROM US.

Also, evidence for the original explosion has been obtained by the detection of MICROWAVES which were produced as a by product of this historic happening. Even today these microwaves can be detected as interference on a poorly tuned TV.

WAVES, LIGHT, OPTICAL FIBRES, SIGNALS AND ULTRASOUND

FEATURES OF WAVES ...
may be transverse eg. light or longitudinal eg. sound.

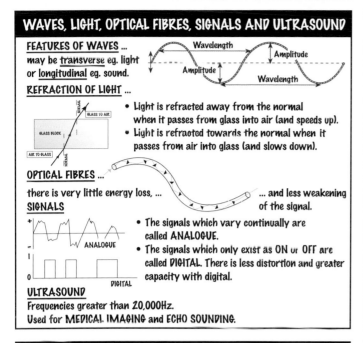

Wavelength
Amplitude
Amplitude
Wavelength

REFRACTION OF LIGHT ...

- Light is refracted away from the normal when it passes from glass into air (and speeds up).
- Light is refracted towards the normal when it passes from air into glass (and slows down).

OPTICAL FIBRES ...
there is very little energy loss, ... and less weakening of the signal.

SIGNALS

ANALOGUE
DIGITAL

- The signals which vary continually are called ANALOGUE.
- The signals which only exist as ON or OFF are called DIGITAL. There is less distortion and greater capacity with digital.

ULTRASOUND
Frequencies greater than 20,000Hz.
Used for MEDICAL IMAGING and ECHO SOUNDING.

ELECTROMAGNETIC WAVES

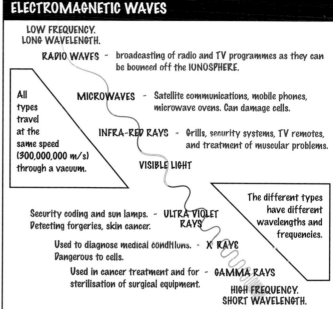

LOW FREQUENCY.
LONG WAVELENGTH.

RADIO WAVES - broadcasting of radio and TV programmes as they can be bounced off the IONOSPHERE.

All types travel at the same speed (300,000,000 m/s) through a vacuum.

MICROWAVES - Satellite communications, mobile phones, microwave ovens. Can damage cells.

INFRA-RED RAYS - Grills, security systems, TV remotes, and treatment of muscular problems.

VISIBLE LIGHT

Security coding and sun lamps. - **ULTRA VIOLET RAYS**
Detecting forgeries, skin cancer.

Used to diagnose medical conditions. - **X RAYS**
Dangerous to cells.

Used in cancer treatment and for - **GAMMA RAYS**
sterilisation of surgical equipment.

HIGH FREQUENCY.
SHORT WAVELENGTH.

The different types have different wavelengths and frequencies.

ATOMIC STRUCTURE AND RADIOACTIVITY

THE ATOM

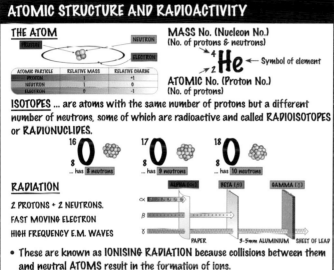

NEUTRON
PROTON
ELECTRON

ATOMIC PARTICLE	RELATIVE MASS	RELATIVE CHARGE
PROTON	1	+1
NEUTRON	1	0
ELECTRON	0	-1

MASS No. (Nucleon No.)
(No. of protons & neutrons)

$$^4_2\text{He}$$ ← Symbol of element

ATOMIC No. (Proton No.)
(No. of protons)

ISOTOPES ... are atoms with the same number of protons but a different number of neutrons, some of which are radioactive and called RADIOISOTOPES or RADIONUCLIDES.

$^{16}_8$O ... has 8 neutrons
$^{17}_8$O ... has 9 neutrons
$^{18}_8$O ... has 10 neutrons

RADIATION

ALPHA (α)   BETA (β)   GAMMA (γ)

α 2 PROTONS + 2 NEUTRONS.
β FAST MOVING ELECTRON
γ HIGH FREQUENCY E.M. WAVES

PAPER   3-5mm ALUMINIUM   SHEET OF LEAD

- These are known as IONISING RADIATION because collisions between them and neutral ATOMS result in the formation of ions.
- Radioactive decay occurs when UNSTABLE NUCLEI disintegrate emitting radiation. This process occurs at random amongst the atoms in the radioactive substance.

USES AND DANGERS OF RADIATION

USES OF RADIOACTIVE ISOTOPES ...
Sterilisation of medical instruments using gamma rays.
Cancer treatment using gamma rays in careful doses.
Smoke detectors use α particles because of their ionising properties.
β and γ cause less ionisation.

DANGERS ... Damage to cells through ionisation can cause CANCER. Only β and γ can penetrate the tissues from outside of the body, but from inside (eg. inhalation into the lungs) α is the most dangerous since it is the most strongly ionising. Workers in the nuclear industry wear safety badges containing photographic film. Ionising radiation can also cause mutations in the genetic material of cells. This can cause defects in future generations.

BACKGROUND RADIATION ...

FROM FOOD
RADON GAS
X RAYS
COSMIC RAYS
NUCLEAR INDUSTRY
MEDICAL

DISPOSAL OF WASTE ...
- Waste products can remain radioactive for thousands of years.
- Low, intermediate and high level waste.
- High level waste is IMMOBILISED in glass in steel containers.
- Intermediate waste is immobilised in cement in steel containers.

GRAVITY, SATELLITES, THE UNIVERSE AND LIFE OF STARS

GRAVITATIONAL FIELD STRENGTH ... differs from planet to planet
WEIGHT (N) = **MASS** (kg) x **GRAVITATIONAL FIELD STRENGTH** (N/kg)
It causes the moon and artificial satellites to orbit the Earth and the Earth and other planets to orbit the Sun.

- It also causes the peculiarly elliptical orbit of comets.
- Our Sun is one star out of many millions of stars in our galaxy, the Milky Way which is one of many billions in the Universe.
- Stars were formed from clouds of collapsing dust and gas, pulled together by gravity. This cloud is called a NEBULA.

LIFE CYCLE OF A STAR

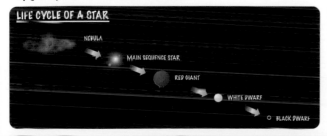

NEBULA
MAIN SEQUENCE STAR
RED GIANT
WHITE DWARF
BLACK DWARF

LIFE IN THE EXPANDING UNIVERSE

COLLECTING EVIDENCE FOR LIFE ...

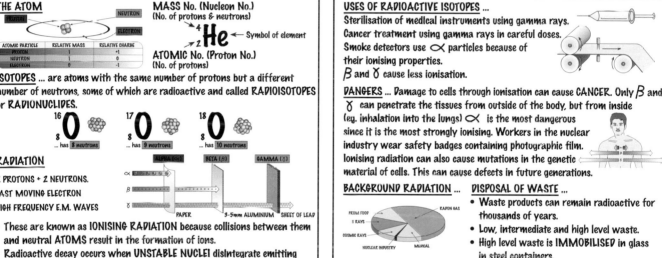

Actually travel to Mars or Europa and look for signs of life!
Could take many months to get to Mars though!

Use robots to travel to Mars or Europa and bring back samples.
Not as reliable as humans!

Use robots to travel to Mars or Europa and take pictures!
Pictures might not come out!

ANALYSING THE EVIDENCE ...
- Samples of rock and dust can be placed inside a sealed container and the atmosphere monitored for changes which could be attributed to life processes eg. respiration.
- SETI analyses radiowaves for patterns. No luck in 40 years.

ORIGIN AND FUTURE OF THE UNIVERSE ...
'STEADY STATE' v 'BIG BANG'. Expanding universe supports the latter. The amount of matter in the universe will decide whether it expands forever or collapses due to gravity.

EVIDENCE FOR THE ORIGIN OF THE UNIVERSE ...

1. 'Red Shift'. Wavelengths of distant galaxies are longer than expected which means the galaxies are moving away
2. Microwave afterglow of the 'big bang' can be detected on TV screens.

INDEX